AA

British Road Map
PUZZLE
BOOK

AA

British Road Map
PUZZLE
BOOK

Written by
Helen Brocklehurst

SPHERE

First published in Great Britain in 2019 by Sphere

1 3 5 7 9 10 8 6 4 2

A CIP catalogue record for this book is available from the British Library.

ISBN 978-0-7515-7897-3

Printed and bound in Italy by L.E.G.O. S.p.A

Papers used by Sphere are from well-managed forests and other
responsible sources.

SPHERE
an imprint of
Little, Brown Book Group
Carmelite House
50 Victoria Embankment
London EC4Y 0DZ

An Hachette UK Company

www.hachette.co.uk

www.littlebrown.co.uk

Contents

A Brief History of Britain's Roads

cAD50 – first main Roman road, the Fosse Way, is built, linking Exeter and Lincoln

1610 – first recorded stagecoach route from Edinburgh to Leith. Stagecoaches were so called because they travelled in 'stages' of ten to fifteen miles

1635 – Charles I makes the postal service available to the public and sets out the main post roads

1657 – first public stagecoach service begins

1663 – first turnpike trust is set up to maintain Britain's first toll road, a section of the Great North Road between Wadesmill in Hertfordshire and Stilton in Huntingdonshire

1707 – Turnpike Act of Parliament ratifies the turnpike trust system

1725 – General George Wade starts to build his network of military roads in the Scottish Highlands, with Major William Caulfeild taking over from him in 1737

1756 – Parliament passes a law enforcing traffic to drive on left on London Bridge

1776 – milestones and directions at crossings become obligatory on all turnpikes under the General Turnpike Act

1781 – world's first wrought-iron bridge opens at Coalbrookdale

1784 – first mail coach set up by John Palmer on the London–Bristol road, delivering the postal mail in the same amount of time as it took passengers to travel

1815 – Scottish engineer Thomas Telford is appointed to improve the old London–Holyhead road, and pioneers new bridge-building techniques, all of which significantly reduce journey times

1816 – first treatise written by Scottish engineer John McAdam, advising on how to improve road surfaces. His method of covering crushed stones with a drainable gravel surface and using a camber (convex road surface) for rainwater to drain off, becomes known as 'macadamisation'

1835 – the General Highways Act states that roads are to be maintained by paid road workers and surveyors

1839–43 – the Rebecca Riots rage in Wales due to farmers finding their livelihoods threatened by the turnpike tolls

1844 – the Turnpikes Act amalgamates the Welsh trusts and reduces tolls in response to the turnpike riots

1850s – steam-powered road locomotives and traction engines are commercially produced

1865 – the Locomotive Act, known as the Red Flag Act, sets the speed motorcars can travel at 4 mph. They have to be preceded by a footman carrying a red flag

1885 – Karl Benz invents the petrol-powered automobile

1896 – the Locomotives on Highways Act repeals the previous requirement of a person needing to precede the vehicle and increases the speed limit to 14 mph

1903 – the new Motor Car Act increases the speed limit to 20 mph

1904 – first number plates introduced, just one or two letters and one number

1905 – The Automobile Association is founded

1906 – The AA begins erecting village signs as local councils don't consider this their responsibility. The AA's distinctive black and yellow signage accounted for the vast majority of signage before 1939

1909 – The AA starts to erect warning signs (school nearby, dangerous bend etc)

1912 – first AA telephone boxes are put up, initially to shelter patrolmen. Later, members could make free local calls from them. AA telephones were only decommissioned in 2002 with the rise of mobile phones

1918 – introduction of white lines painted on the roads to help reduce accidents. The practice is standardised in 1926

1922 – British roads are numbered for the first time under the new National Classification Scheme. A definitive list is published a year later

1926 – first electric traffic light installed on the corner of St James's Street, Piccadilly, in London

1934 – longest road tunnel opens, the Mersey Tunnel, running 2.87 miles (4.62 km) in length

1935 – Percy Shaw's famous headlight-reflecting Cat's Eyes first used. Before that, The AA had marked the road edges with reflective marker posts

1958 – first section of motorway opens, the short 5 mile (8 km) Preston bypass (M6)

1964 – the modern signage system we have today is established in the Traffic Signs Regulations and General Directions

1965 – national speed limit of 70 mph introduced

1966 – longest bridge opened, the A92 Tay Road Bridge, crossing the Firth and stretching 1.4 miles (2.2 km)

1967 – reflective number plates introduced

1972 – Swindon's infamous 'magic roundabout' opens

1983 – wearing of seatbelts becomes compulsory for front passengers. It only becomes compulsory for rear seatbelts to be worn in 1991

1986 – Britain's busiest motorway, the M25, opens

1992 – first speed camera installed

2002 – first congestion charge system introduced in Durham, and a year later in London

2003 – first toll motorway opens, the M6 Toll road, bypassing the busiest section of the M6 around Birmingham

AA Map Symbols

[M4]	Motorway with number	H	24-hour Accident & Emergency hospital
[Toll] T4 Toll	Toll motorway with toll station	C	Crematorium
5	Restricted motorway junctions	P+R	Park and Ride (at least 6 days per week)
Fleet S R	Motorway service area, rest area		City, town, village or other built-up area
K	Motorway and junction under construction		National boundary, county or administrative boundary
A3	Primary route single/dual carriageway		Scenic route
11	Primary route junction with and without number	_i_ _i_	Tourist Information Centre (all year/seasonal)
3	Restricted primary route junctions	V	Visitor or heritage centre
S	Primary route service area	⊕	Caravan site (AA inspected)
BATH	Primary route destination	▲	Camping site (AA inspected)
A1123	Other A road single/dual carriageway	▲⊕	Caravan & camping site (AA inspected)
B2070	B road single/dual carriageway	♨	Abbey, cathedral or priory
	Minor road, more than 4 metres wide, less than 4 metres wide	♨.	Ruined abbey, cathedral or priory
✚ ✚ ✚	Roundabout	✗ ⌂	Castle, historic house or building
✚ ✚ ✚	Interchange/junction	⌂	Museum or art gallery
	Narrow primary/other A/B road with passing places (Scotland)	⊞	Industrial interest
	Road under construction	⊓	Aqueduct or viaduct

Road tunnel		Garden, arboretum
Road toll, steep gradient (arrows point downhill)		Vineyard, brewery or distillery
Distance in miles between symbols		Country park, theme park
Railway line, in tunnel		Agricultural showground
Railway/tram station, level crossing		Farm or animal centre
Tourist railway		Zoological or wildlife collection
Height in metres, mountain pass		Bird collection, aquarium
Snow gates (on main routes)		RSPB site
Vehicle ferry		National Nature Reserve (England, Scotland, Wales)
Fast vehicle ferry or catamaran		Local nature reserve, Wildlife Trust reserve
Airport (major/minor), heliport		Forest drive
International freight terminal		National trail
English Heritage site		National Park and National Scenic Area (Scotland)
Historic Scotland site		Forest Park
Cadw (Welsh heritage) site		Heritage coast
Major shopping centre, other place of interest		
Attraction within urban area		
World Heritage Site (UNESCO)		

628 ▲ 637 Lecht Summit

Mileage chart

The mileage chart shows distances in miles between two towns along AA-recommended routes. Using motorways and other main roads this is normally the fastest route, though not necessarily the shortest.

The journey times are shown in hours and minutes. These times should be used as a guide only and do not allow for unforeseen traffic delays, rest breaks or fuel stops.

For example, the 376 miles (605 km) journey between Glasgow and Norwich should take approximately 6 hours 45 minutes.

Journey times

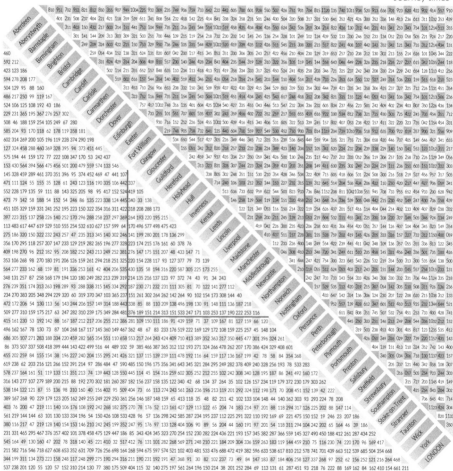

Distances in miles (one mile equals 1.6093 km)

Types of Puzzle

There are forty puzzles in this book, each containing ten questions and illustrated with an AA map. Many of these have been taken from The AA's archive to illustrate how road-mapping has evolved over the last century.

Each puzzle has some quiz questions to test your general knowledge. In many cases, there will be clues, such as date references or information in the introductions and maps to help you answer these, but often a good guess will be required. Some questions will test your driving skills and knowledge of the highway code and road signs. There are also some questions based on place names, which require either excellent general knowledge or some good inference to answer.

Other questions are purely based on your observations of the map, and your map-reading skills. These include questions about alternative routes, map scales and gradients. The maths and number puzzles do not require advanced maths, but will test your problem-solving and logic skills.

Finally, there are word puzzles, including word searches, straight anagrams and cryptic clues (which often, but not always, contain anagrams). For example, the clue 'Quite different to rogan josh' suggests an anagram of 'TO ROGAN JOSH'. The answer is JOHN O'GROATS. The answers can all be found within the map, and some questions are designed to be more challenging than others.

The questions are not graded by difficulty, but as every puzzler has a different set of knowledge and skills, you will find some easier than others. We hope you enjoy the challenge and learn something along the way. Good luck, and happy puzzling!

PUZZLES

EARLIEST ROADS

In ancient times, the main routes across Britain were used for driving animals to market (drovers' roads) and for pilgrimage between sacred places, such as Avebury and Stonehenge. Many of these old ways still exist today as footpaths for walkers. The oldest of these long-distance paths – at least 5,000 years old – is thought to be the Ridgeway. Probably constructed as a trading route, it runs across Wiltshire and Berkshire, and was later used by invading armies and drovers. Another pre-Roman cross-country route, known as the Icknield Way, meets the Ridgeway and runs all the way to Norfolk.

The ancient trackway known since Victorian times as the Pilgrims' Way is probably about 3,000 years old. It provides a pilgrimage route from Winchester to the shrine of Thomas Becket in Canterbury. The route signed today exists over the stone-age traffic artery running over the North Downs.

The first major road builders were, of course, the Romans. Organised infrastructure was vital for the expansion and maintenance of the empire. In Britain they constructed about 2,000 miles of paved roads built straight for speed and a clear line of sight. Four ancient roads were named in the Laws of Edward the Confessor as royal highways. They were the two main Roman roads running out of London – Watling Street and Ermine Street – and the two major cross-country routes: the Fosse Way, which ran from Devon to Lincoln, and the Icknield Way. These roads were so well constructed that they continued to be used for years after the Romans and, as you'll see in the next quizzes, they have evolved into some of our major roads today.

Opposite: Roger Roberts / Fosse Way southwest of Malmesbury / CC BY-SA 2.0

There are many types of the king's peace;
. . . another which the four roads have, that is Watling
Street, Fosse Way, Iknield Street, and Ermine Street, of
which two extend for the length of the kingdom, the
others across the width.

The Laws of Edward the Confessor
(*Leges Edwardi Confessoris*)

ERMINE STREET

Running from Londinium (London) to Eboracum (York) via Lindum Colonia (Lincoln), Ermine Street was the main Roman road leading north out of the capital. It was named after the Earningas ('Eagle's people') who lived in the part of Cambridgeshire that the road passed through. Such is the historic importance of Ermine Street that the route out of London as far as Godmanchester became known as the Old North Road. Centuries later, many parts form the line of the current A1 and it was a precursor of the Great North Road (*see Puzzle 5*).

The road began at Bishopsgate, one of five gates in the Roman wall surrounding London, each of which marked the start of a main road. Ermine Street (and the Old North Road) ran north through Shoreditch High Street, Stoke Newington High Street, and along the A10 towards Royston.

The Newport Arch in Lincoln, built along this road, is the only remaining Roman archway in Britain. North of Lincoln, just past Caenby Corner, a long stretch of Ermine Street remains as the A15 (*see Puzzle 37*), continuing to Winteringham on the south shore of the Humber estuary. The Romans would have crossed the estuary by ferry here, and from the north shore the road continued on to York. Elsewhere, Dere Street provided a continuation of Ermine Street, running from York to the Antonine Wall in Scotland.

MAP 01

1. Ermine Street started at Bishopsgate, but can you name any of the other Roman gates in walled Londinium?

2. The Old North Road (A10) coming out of London is also known as Great --------- Road?

3. Which place on the map is an anagram of CHARTED GNOMES?

4. Which place on this map shares its name with the first person to introduce the printing press in Britain?

5. Which three historic counties are shown on the map?

6. Aside from Ermine Street, which other one of Edward the Confessor's royal roads is labelled on this map?

7. What is the sum total of the road numbers for those roads simply marked 'Roman Road' on this map? Express the answer in Roman numerals.

8. Using the mileage indicators shown in blue circles on the map, what is the approximate distance from Cambridge to Baldock?

9. What alternative name is given for the Ouse on this map?

10. Betting when about fifty, indeed!

Opposite: Extract from *The Reader's Digest AA Book of the Road, 3rd Edition* (1972) © The Reader's Digest Association Limited, 1966. The map shows the Ermine Street of the A10 to Royston and the A14 (now the A1198) to Godmanchester. You can see how the Old North Road (Ermine Street) and Great North Road converge at Alconbury and continue north on what is today the A1(M).

Watling Street /wŏtˈlĭng/

noun

The name 'Watling Street' is said to have its roots in 'Vitellina Strata', meaning 'the road of Vitellius' envisioned by the Roman Emperor Vitellius and constructed during his reign.

WATLING STREET

For the truth of the expression 'all roads lead to Rome' you need look no further than Watling Street. This precursor of the modern A2 (*see Puzzle 6*) ran southeast from a crossroads in London near the Elephant all the way to Dover. It then continued across the Channel and over the Alps until it reached Rome. It also prefigured the modern A5 (*see Puzzle 10*), continuing northwest from Marble Arch all the way to Wroxeter.

The Battle of Watling Street has gone down in history as one of Britain's bloodiest battles and is thought to have taken place somewhere between London and Wroxeter in AD 60 or AD 61. Boudica led the uprising of the Britons against the Romans in the south but her larger army suffered heavy losses at the hands of the more capable opposing force, and she allegedly poisoned herself following her defeat.

This section of mapping shows that the A5 takes the course of the Roman Watling Street from Milton Keynes, where the grid road system incorporates Watling Street as V4 (*see Puzzle 32*). The A5 returns to the Roman route just north of Stony Stratford and through Towcester all the way to junction 17 of the M1, near to the Watford Gap, that time-honoured marker of where north meets south.

MAP 02

1.   The Watford Gap is the site of which motorway first?

2.   Which famous racecourse is located on Watling Street?

3.   Which monument, depicted on this map, was built by King Edward I to mark one of the twelve places where his wife's body rested on her funeral procession from Lincoln to London?

4.   Cosgrove 'Iron Trunk' aqueduct was built for which canal to pass over which river?

5.   What is the approximate distance shown on the map between Stony Stratford and Towcester?

6.   Silverstone sits by what kind of junction on the A43?

7.   Which place on Watling Street is an anagram of COUNTED?

8.   Which is the shorter route from Stony Stratford to Watford: the M1 or the A5?

9.   Which two sporting grounds in Northampton can be seen on this map?

10.   The sound of one popping up at breakfast time?

Opposite: Extract from *The AA Great Britain Road Atlas 2020* (2019) at a scale of 1:200,000.

Kirby
West Haddon
Coton Manor
Coton Ravensthorpe
Teeton
Brixworth
Scaldwell
Walgrave
Hannington
Little Harrowden
Great Harrow
Watford
A428
Spratton
Pitsford Water
Holcot
Hardwick
Watford Gap
B5385
Long Buckby
East Haddon
Holdenby House
Holdenby
Brixworth
Northampton & Lamport Railway
Pitsford Reservoir
Pitsford
Sywell
A508
Wellingbo
Mears Ashby
Wilby
Whilton
Great Brington
Little Brington
Church Brampton
Chapel Brampton
Moulton
Boughton
Overstone
Sywell Reservoir
New Barto
Norton
B4036
Brockhall
Nobottle
Althorp Park
Harlestone
A5076
Kingsthorpe
Boothville
Kingsley Park
Great Billing
Ecton
A45
Ea Ba
Coventry
A5
M1
Dodford
Flore
Harpole
A428
New Duston
Dallington
NORTHAMPTON
Queen's Park
Weston Favell
Little Billing
Cogenhoe
Whist
A45
Weedon Bec
Stowehill
Harpole
Duston
A4500
St James's End
Abington
Little Houghton
Lower End
Brafield-on-the-Green
Denton
Upper Weedon
Lower Weedon
Nether Heyford
Upper Heyford
Kislingbury
Upton
Swan Valley
Far Cotton
Eleanor Cross
Hardingstone
Great Houghton
A428
Church Stowe
Bugbrooke
Rothersthorpe
Northampton
15A
Hunsbury Hill
A45
Wootton
Preston Deanery
Hackleton
Upper Stowe
Farthingstone
Gayton
Milton Malsor
Collingtree
Grange Park
Quinton
Horton
Litchborough
Pattishall
Eastcote
Astcote
Blisworth
Quinton Green
Piddington
B526
Maidford
Cold Higham
Tiffield
Courteenhall
Roade
Salcey
Ravenstone
Quinbury End
Foxley
Duncote
Caldecote
Stoke Bruerne
Hartwell
Salcey Forest
Stoke Goldington
We Under
Blakesley
Shutlanger
Ashton
Woodend
Greens Norton
Hulcote
The Canal
A508
Long Street
Ty
Weedon Lois
Bradden
Stoke Park Pavilions
Grafton Regis
Gayhurst
Slapton
Foscote
Towcester
Alderton
Hanslope
Tathall End
Newpo Pagne
Milthorpe
Wood Burcote
Paulerspury
Yardley Gobion
Little Linford
Haversham
Abthorpe
Wappenham
Pury End
Plumpton End
A5
Furtho
Castlethorpe
Newport Pagnell
Great Linford
elmdon
Silverstone
Whittlebury
Potterspury
Puxley
Old Stratford
Cosgrove
New Bradwell
Wolverton
Bradwell
Falcut
A43
Silverstone
A413
Lillingstone Lovell
Old Wolverton
MILTON KEYNES
Syresham
Brackley Hatch
Lillingstone Dayrell
Deanshanger
Stony Stratford
Passenham
Xscape
Crowfield
Pimlico
Biddlesden
Wicken
Calverton
Upper Weald
Loughton
tone
Whitfield
Dadford
Stowe Gardens
Leckhampstead
Beachampton
Shenley Church End
H
Turweston
Shalstone
Chackmore
Maids Moreton
Akeley
Thornton
Shenley Brook End
Whaddon
Bletch
Fen Bletchley
Westbury
evenley
A422
Water Stratford
Buckingham
Radclive
Nash
Mixbury
Finmere
Tingewick
Gawcott
Thornborough
A421
Singleborough
Great Horwood
Thrift Farm
B403
Newt Long
Newton Purcell
Hethe
Barton Hartshorn
Chetwode
Padbury
Preston
Adstock
A413
Little Horwood
Drayton

Mapping milestone

In 1906 we began erecting village road signs. The first
AA sign was erected at Hatfield, showing the place
name and mileages to nearby towns. In 1939 local
councils took new responsibility for erecting village
road signs. The AA had already put up more than
30,000 of them by this time.

THE FOSSE WAY

How do you build a road? The reason that Roman roads endured was due in no small part to their construction. At the base, sand was laid, followed by a layer of stone slabs in cement, on top of which sat a layer of crushed stones in cement, and finally, on top, stone paving. There was a drainage ditch, or 'fosse' on each side, from which the Fosse Way gets its name.

In fact, it may have been a defensive ditch, because the road marked the western boundary of Roman rule. Linking Isca Dumnoniorum (Exeter) with Lindum Colonia (Lincoln) through 182 miles of remarkably straight road, it joined Akeman Street at Cirencester, Ermine Street (*see Puzzle 1*) at Lincoln, Icknield Street at Bourton-on-the-Water, and Watling Street (*see Puzzle 2*) at Wigston Parva, just south of Leicester.

The Fosse Way met both Akeman Street and the Ermin Way at Cirencester (Ermin Way, not to be confused with Ermine Street, connected Cirencester with Gloucester.) The map for this puzzle shows the section of the Fosse Way from Cirencester along the A429 to Halford. You can see the road continue on what is today the B4455 from Halford. The road continues beyond the map to meet the A5 (Watling Street) around Wigston Parva.

MAP 03

1. Place names ending '-cester' and '-chester', such as Cirencester, are common along Roman roads. They are derived from the Latin 'castra', meaning what?

2. What can be found at Chedworth, constructed between the 2nd and 4th centuries and now owned by the National Trust?

3. A motor museum, including a toy collection, can be found in which town along this section of the Fosse Way?

4. Which place on the map is an anagram of BAD FROST?

5. Which two villages sound like they belong in a crime novel?

6. Which places with Fosse in their name can be seen on this map?

7. Two rivers lend their name to a number of places along their route. Which are they, and how many places can you see named after them?

8. Which key defence station appears on the map?

9. Given that a 20 mm grid square equates to 5 km, estimate the distance a train would travel from Shipton-under-Wychwood to Evesham.

10. Unusual tea drunk here?

Opposite: Extract from *The AA Great Britain Road Atlas 2020* (2019), reproduced at a scale of 1:250,000.

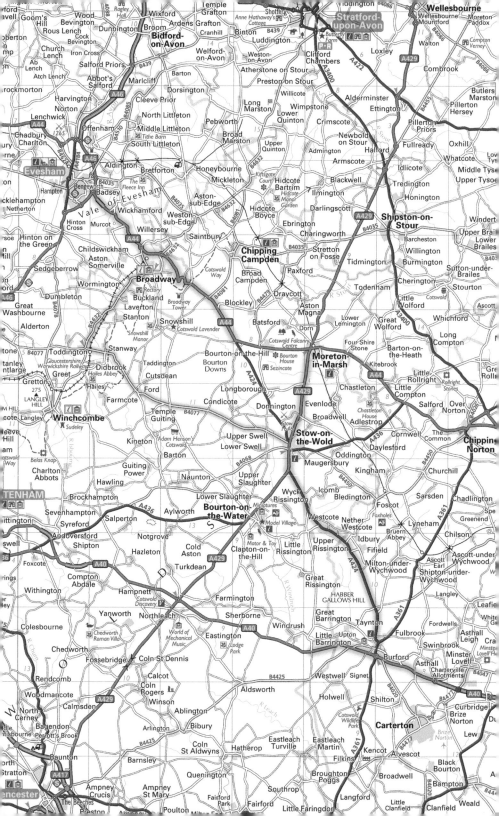

Hogback /ˈhɒgbak/
[also, Hog's Back]

noun

A long hill or mountain ridge with steep sides.

THE HOG'S BACK
A31

Located along the ancient Pilgrims' Way (*see p.19*), the Hog's Back is a long, narrow ridge, situated between the Surrey towns of Guildford and Farnham. At some point in history, it must have reminded someone of the back of a pig, though we don't know when the current name came into being; it was Guildown in medieval times, but had taken its current name by the nineteenth century. In a letter to her sister, Jane Austen referred to her journey over 'the Hogsback' as providing excellent views of the South Downs.

The elevated position of the ridge made for a good road, offering travellers a panorama over the country as far as London to the east and Hindhead to the south. It formed part of the ancient royal highway between London and Winchester, although today the Pilgrims' Way footpath deviates from the top of the Hog's Back, wisely avoiding the modern A31.

The original road was the part of the dual carriageway that runs east to west. An additional carriageway on which the traffic runs west to east was added in the early 1970s.

MAP 04

1. The mansion once known as Poyle Hill House near the village of Seale (now the AA-rated Hog's Back Hotel & Spa), was once the Admiralty semaphore station. In what way did its situation make it perfect for this use?

2. Which National Trail path, created in 1978, runs parallel with the Hog's Back?

3. Walk down The Street and you might see a blaze of colour from the azaleas and rhododendrons at which National Trust site?

4. Which tributary of the River Thames has two branches that join at Tilford?

5. Counties used to be split into administrative divisions called 'hundreds'. Which three 'hundreds' met at the Hog's Back?

6. Which hill shares its name with a sinister-sounding word game?

7. What does the 'ham' in Farnham, Tongham and Puttenham mean?

8. What is the sum total of the primary routes on the map?

9. Which place on the map is an anagram of LOWER PONDS?

10. Right thing to do with a large map?

Opposite: Extract from *The AA Close-Up Britain Atlas, 2nd edition* (2008) at a scale of 1:100,000. Hog's Back is clearly marked, as is the North Downs Way National Trail.

TRANSPORT REVOLUTIONS

The Royal Mail, established by Henry VII in 1516 for royal use and then made available to the public by Charles I in 1635, routed most mail through London because the Roman roads were still the best in the country. Until Tudor times, the monasteries had generally looked after the upkeep of the roads. After their dissolution, the responsibility for road maintenance shifted to the parishes. By and large, this proved unsuccessful, with roads remaining pot-holed and rutted, dusty in summer and impassably muddy in winter. The first public stagecoach service began in 1657, but with the roads in such a poor state, the coaches usually only ran for a few months of the year. Journeys were arduous and unreliable, and travellers were at risk from highwaymen.

It wasn't until the eighteenth century that road building really began in earnest again. It was the coming of the first toll roads – the turnpikes – that started to improve the road network, and massively decreased journey times. Initially, there was public uproar over people having to pay to use the same roads they always had, leading to turnpike riots all over the country. But seeing traffic levels continuing to rise, the new turnpike trusts were viewed as a sound investment by canny entrepreneurs, and by 1770 they'd given rise to 15,000 new miles of road. John McAdam led the road engineering, insisting on proper foundations, proper surfacing and a convex shape for drainage. Milestones were a new statutory provision, and traffic had to drive on the left.

New mail coaches significantly decreased journey times between major cities, and new packhorse routes, which had developed to move a new range of manufactured goods around the country, created more cross-country routes. The need to construct new roads through challenging cross-country terrain led to some remarkable feats of engineering, most notably from Thomas Telford on his London to Holyhead route through the mountains of North Wales.

Opposite: Menai Suspension Bridge / David Dixon / CC BY-SA 2.0

*He strolled about the country as ragged as a colt, till
he met with a waggoner who was going to London, and
who gave him leave to walk all the way by the side of his
waggon without paying anything for his passage, which
pleased little Whittington very much, as he wanted to see
London badly, for he had heard that the streets
were paved with gold . . .*

The History of Whittington (1892)

THE GREAT NORTH ROAD
A1

The Great North Road was used for years as a main arterial route from London to Edinburgh. Today it is better known as the A1, which stretches 410 miles and is Britain's longest numbered road. In the early days of the stagecoach, the Great North Road terminated at York, taking about four days. In 1656 the cost of maintaining the Great North Road was so high that the boroughs of Hertfordshire, Huntington and Cambridgeshire faced bankruptcy, and lobbied parliament for the right to raise tolls.

They were successful, and in 1663 it became Britain's first turnpike road. By the golden coaching era of the nineteenth century, the journey time had shortened to twenty hours, but travellers could now continue all the way to Edinburgh via Boroughbridge.

Starting at Smithfield Market, it went north via the Angel Inn, an important staging post in Angel, and on through Highgate, Hatfield and Alconbury, where it picked up the former Ermine Street route (*see Puzzle 1*). Alconbury saw the meeting of the Great North Road and the Old North Road, and a milestone still exists showing the distances by each route to London.

The section of the Great North Road shown in the map that follows picks up the road from Alconbury at junction 14 of the A1(M) and follows it all the way to Great Casterton/Stamford A1.

MAP 05

1. Which pantomime hero famously travelled the Great North Road to find fortune in London?

2. Which railway line stops at Ferry Meadows?

3. The Great North Road was allegedly the escape route for which notorious highwayman who supposedly rode overnight from London to York in under fifteen hours?

4. Which National Nature Reserve situated close to the A1(M) is an important lowland wood?

5. Given the map is at a scale of 1:200,000, what is the approximate distance from Godmanchester to Great Casterton?

6. Which poem by T.S. Eliot can be found on the map?

7. Which interchange on the A1 was once the site of a prisoner-of-war camp built during the Napoleonic Wars and sited far enough along the Great North Road to prevent any prisoner escaping to the coast?

8. Whose song 'Heading South on the Great North Road' paid tribute to the travellers throughout history who took this route for its promise of a better life?

9. Which place on the map is an anagram of CONNOTING?

10. As rugby spectators at Twickenham did?

Opposite: Extract from *The AA Great Britain Road Atlas 2020* (2019) at a scale of 1:200,000.

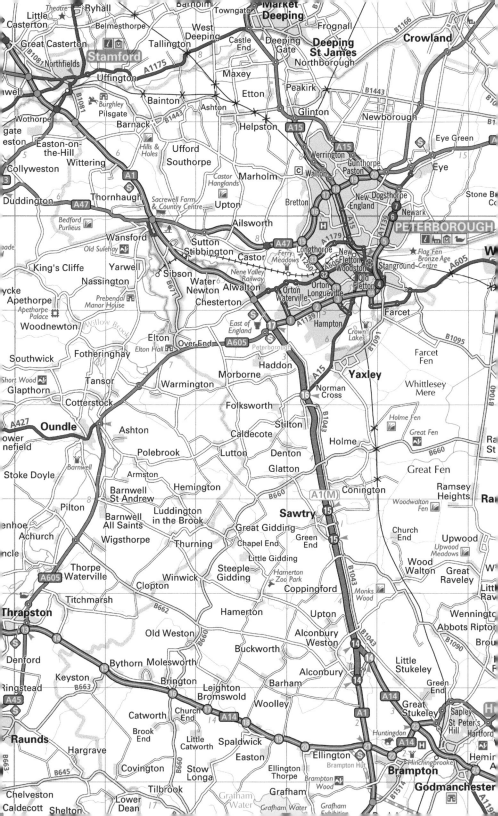

About the map

This extract from an old *AA Members Touring Guide*, mapped at ten miles to the inch, clearly shows the line of the A2. The line of the road is remarkably straight, despite the fact that over time the road deviated from its original course. Today the only stretch of road that can really be said to follow the old Roman road is that which runs between Rochester and Springhead, near Gravesend.

THE GREAT DOVER ROAD
A2

The Great Dover Road roughly followed the Roman route of Watling Street (*see Puzzle 2*), linking London with Canterbury (Durovernum Cantiacorum), and the three Kentish ports now known as Richborough (near Sandwich), Dover and Lympne (near Hythe). Two bridges – London Bridge and Rochester Bridge – were constructed by the Romans.

Gradually the road, which had fallen into disrepair, was restored in the eighteenth century as sections were converted into turnpike roads. In the nineteenth century, it was rebranded as the Great Dover Road and the new industrial age began to make its mark with a cast-iron rebuild of Rochester Bridge (1856), and the completion of Tower Bridge (1894) and the Blackwall Tunnel (1897).

With the 1920s road classification scheme, the route became known as the A2. It remained the main artery for London traffic into Kent, prior to the opening of the M2 (1963–65), which relieved the volume of traffic on the route.

MAP 06

1. In which famous collection of Middle English stories does a group of pilgrims have a storytelling competition as they travel from London to Canterbury along this road?

2. Which five ports in Kent and Sussex together formed the Anglo-Saxon Cinque Ports?

3. The A207 follows the line of old Watling Street through which three minor destinations, indicated on the map with white circles, before reaching Dartford?

4. Given the scale as shown on the map, estimate the distance from Sittingbourne to Dover along the A2.

5. Anagram of which place DOMINATES?

6. Thomas Ingoldsby wrote that, 'The World, according to the best geographers, is divided into Europe, Asia, Africa, America, and . . . ' which fifth continent?

7. Which 'rushing river' separates 'sheep island' from mainland Kent?

8. 'Gate' in a place name probably referred to gaps in the cliffs that give rise to pools of water. Name the gates you can find on the map.

9. What do North Foreland, Ramsgate, South Foreland, Dover, Folkestone and Dungeness have in common?

10. Save someone's bacon?

Opposite: See p.42 for details of the map.

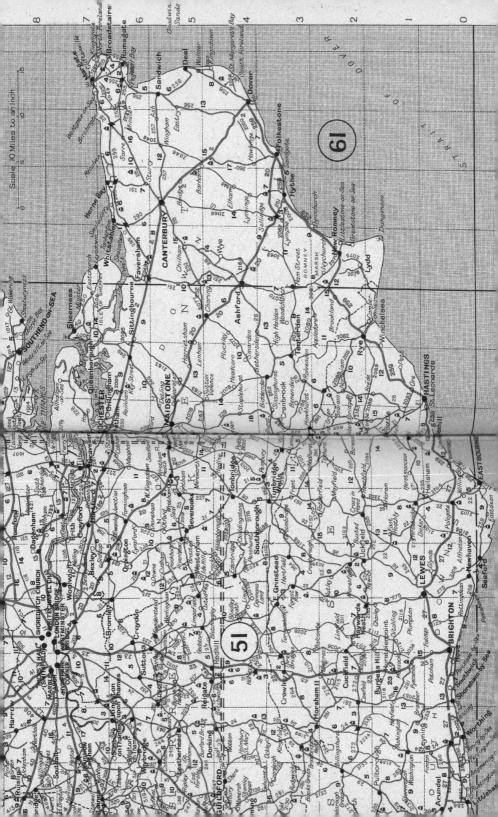

> *The great road from London to Falmouth and the Land's End branches off at Exeter, leaves Whitstone, Tedburne St. Mary, and Cheriton Bishops on the right, and Drew's Teignton on the left, passes through Crockernwell, where is a posting house (11 miles from Exeter); thence leaving South Tawton on the right, it passes through South Zeal and Sticklepath to Oakhampton (11 miles) . . .*

Magna Britannia; Being A Concise Topographical Account Of The Several Counties Of Great Britain, Volume 6

THE GREAT ROAD TO LAND'S END
A30

Before the days of the A303 and the M3, the A30 was an important coaching route from London to Land's End and a principal route for the postal service. It was known as 'The Great South-West Road' or, in the 1814 Magna Britannia, as 'The Great Road to Land's End'. Around Camberley it followed the Devil's Highway, an old Roman route that ran from London to Silchester.

As a coaching route, it started at Hyde Park Corner, but today's trunk road begins at Henlys Roundabout near Hounslow and travels a somewhat interrupted 284 miles to Penzance. John Ogilby's strip maps of 1675 showed the road roughly as we know it to Exeter, but following a coastal route to Penzance.

Then, a 'New Direct Road' was created in the early nineteenth century, adapting the route to run via Amesbury along some of the modern A303 (*see Puzzle 24*). A hundred years later, bypasses were built around Basingstoke and Okehampton, and in a few places the road was upgraded to become dual carriageway.

MAP 07

1.   Who wrote the poem 'Meditation on the A30'?

2.   Using the scale bar, estimate the distance between Launceston and Redruth.

3.   Which ridge of hills is included within the Exmoor National Park?

4.   Which three 'tors' are labelled on the map?

5.   Which river marked on the map is a palindrome?

6.   A Charles Kingsley novel is named after this place?

7.   Packhorse bridge over the River Teign on Dartmoor?

8.   The four Norman castles of Cornwall were Launceston, Tintagel, Trematon, and which other, labelled on this map?

9.   Which place on the map is an anagram of DOCTRINE?

10.   Act of regret about that last letter!

Opposite: The line of the A30 in Devon and Cornwall can be seen in this extract from *The AA Road Book of England and Wales* (1938). The road runs through Chard and Honiton down into Exeter and then continues in a reasonably straight line via Launceston, Bodmin and Redruth to Penzance. The map contains no road numbers, despite the A30 having received its nomenclature in 1923 as part of the Ministry of Transport road classification system.

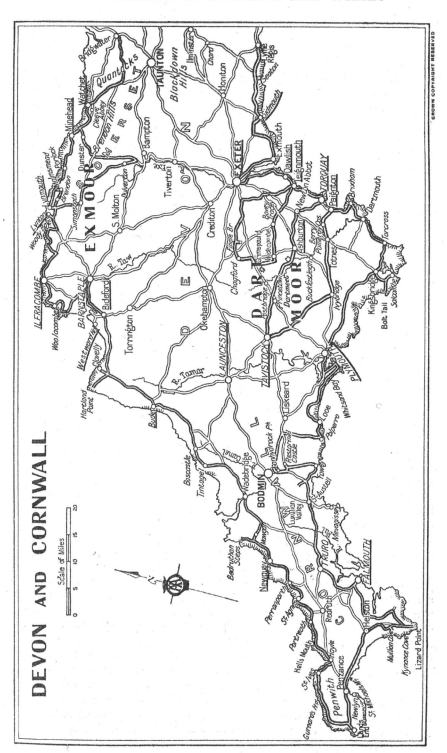

DEVON AND CORNWALL

"

Whereas to this time there hath been no certain or constant intercourse between the Kingdoms of England and Scotland, his Majesty hath been graciously pleased to command his servant, Thomas Witherings Esquire, his Majesties Postmaster of England for foreign parts, to settle a running post or two, to run, night and day, between
Edinburgh in Scotland and the
City of London . . .

. . . The three first conveyances from London to Edinburgh, from London to Westchester and Hollyhead in Wales, and from London to Plymouth and Exeter, are to begin the first week after Michaelmas next.

Royal Proclamation of Charles I (31 July 1635)

"

THE GREAT WEST ROAD
A4

When Charles I made the Royal Mail service available to the public in 1635, he commissioned the 'Great Roads' to be built to facilitate the postal service. The Great Road to Bristol, which evolved into the A4, was one of these, and others formed a blueprint for our modern A1, A2, A3 and A5.

The A4 has its origins in pre-Roman times, and the Great West Road out of London served as a key arterial route throughout history until being superseded by the roughly parallel M4, which opened in 1966.

When Queen Anne made Bath a fashionable destination for the wealthy, the road became known as the Bath Road. Various turnpike trusts were quick to appear over the route, improving road maintenance and journey times.

By 1836, ten stagecoaches a day made the journey to Bath, arriving in eighteen hours. But its golden era was not to last long. The new Great Western Railway, engineered by Brunel, opened in 1840, and by 1848 the stagecoach service had ceased to run.

MAP 08

1. The Roman road to Bath runs around the base of which man-made mound, today in the care of English Heritage?

2. Which ancient footpath, thought to be Britain's oldest road, starts between the villages of Fyfield and West Kennett?

3. How many white horse hill carvings can you see depicted in this section of the map, and what do they tell us about the geology of the area?

4. Which white horse sits near an obelisk known as the Lansdowne Monument?

5. The A4 passes under a bridge between buildings belonging to which famous public school?

6. Which four roads on the map are marked as scenic routes?

7. Given a scale of 1:200,000, or using the mileage indicators, estimate the distance from Hungerford to Chippenham along the A4.

8. Which ten downs are featured on this map?

9. A flight of twenty-nine locks sitting on the Kennet and Avon Canal.

10. Welcome purchase, shopper finally admitted.

Opposite: This section of the A4 between Marlborough and Chippingham (via Silbury Hill) is taken from *The AA Great Britain Road Atlas 2020* (2019) and shown at a scale of 1:200,000.

Hungerford
Marlborough
Devizes
Chippenham
Melksham
Calne
Wootton Bassett
Wroughton
Lyneham

Upper Lambourn
Lambourn
Eastbury
Lambourn Woodlands
Straight Soley
Chilton Foliat
Hastoe
Littledown
Vernham Street
Vernham Dean

B4001
B4192
A338
A4
A346
A345
A342
A361
A360
A365
A3102
A3104
A4192
B4005
B4069
B3087
B3098

Bishopstone
Bishopstone Downs
Hodson
Badbury
Elcombe
Overtown
Uffcott
Broad Town
Clyffe Pypard
Bushton
Broad Hinton
Berwick Bassett
Winterbourne Bassett
Winterbourne Monkton
Rockley
Draycot Foliat
Chiseldon
Upper Upham
Liddington Castle
Aldbourne
Baydon
Preston
Ramsbury
Axford
Woodsend
Whittonditch
Crooked Soley
Knighton
New Town
Littlecote Villa
Froxfield
Little Bedwyn
Chisbury
Chisbury Chapel
Great Bedwyn
Crofton Beam Engines
Crofton
Stibb Green
Burbage
Easton Royal
Easton Hill
Newtown
Shalbourne
Bagshot
Rivar
Buttermere
Oxenwood
Fosbury
Haydown Hill 254
Tidcombe
Tidcombe Down
Collingbourne Kingston
Brunton
Wexcombe
Wilton
East Grafton
West Grafton
Wootton Rivers
Milton Lilbourne
White Horse
Southcott
Pewsey
Manningford Bruce
Manningford Bohune
Fyfield
West Stowell
Huish
Oare
Pewsey Down
Rushall
Upavon
Charlton St Peter
North Newnton
Wilsford
Wilsford Down
Marden
Charlton
Chirton
Conock
Wedhampton
Patney
Hilcott
Woodborough
Broad Street
Honeystreet
Alton Priors
Alton Barnes
Stanton St Bernard
Allington
Bourton
All Cannings
Coate
Horton
Little Horton
Bishops Cannings
Beechingstoke
Etchilhampton
Vale of Pewsey
Nursteed
Stert
Potterne Wick
Urchfont
Eastcott
Marston
Worton
Potterne
Poulshot
Seend
Seend Cleeve
Bulkington
Keevil
The Strand
Great Cheverell
Steeple Ashton
St Edith's Marsh
Rowde
Dunkirk
Caen Hill Locks
Oliver's Castle
Roundway
White Horse
Heddington
Netherstreet
Blackland
Theobald's Green
Stockley
Sandy Lane
Bowood
Derry Hill
Studley
Bromham
Chittoe
Bowden Hill
Sandridge
Westbrook
Redstocks
Sells Green
Inmarsh
Notton
Pewsham
Lacock Abbey
Fox Talbot Museum
Reybridge
Naish Hill
Bromhall
Tytherton Lucas
Bremhill
East Tytherton
Tytherton
Foxham
Charlcutt
Catcomb
Spirthill
Hilmarton
Goatacre
Highway
Clevancy
Preston
Tockenham
Tockenham Wick
Bradenstoke
REME
Christian Malford
Seagry Heath
Lower Seagry
Sutton Benger
Kington Langley
Langley Burrell
West End
East Tytherton
Hardenhuish
Stanton St Quintin
Upper Seagry
Bremhill
Cherhill
Compton Bassett
Yatesbury
Avebury
Avebury Manor
Keiller Museum
Avebury Down
Windmill Hill
Alexander Keiller Museum
Silbury Hill
West Kennett
West Kennett Long Barrow
East Kennett
West Overton
Lockeridge
Fyfield
Clatford
The Sanctuary
Manton
White Horse
Marlinsell
Clench Common
Durley
Savernake Forest
Cadley
Stitchcombe
Mildenhall
Ogbourne Maizey
Ogbourne St Andrew
Ogbourne St George
Southend
Marlborough Downs
Barbury Castle
Ridgeway Path
White Horse
Overtown
Martinsell
Knap Hill
White Horse
Milk Hill 294
Rybury
Morgans Hill 258
Calstone
Cherhill Down
Wellington Down
North Wessex Downs
Trusloe
Beckhampton
Henge & Stone Circles
Westcourt
Aughton

If you had seen these roads before they were made,
You would hold up your hands and bless General Wade.

Anon, ascribed to William Caulfeild

GATEWAY TO THE HIGHLANDS
A82

Following the Jacobite rebellion of 1715, George I charged General George Wade with leading the construction of proper roads, bridges, barracks and garrisons in Scotland to ensure better control. In all, he was responsible for 240 miles of roads and thirty bridges, before being succeeded by William Caulfeild (*see Puzzle 40*).

The road from Inverness to Fort William, which runs along the south side of Loch Ness, was the first of Wade's Military Roads to be constructed. The modern A82, which runs from Glasgow to Inverness via Fort William, is in part a Wade Road, in part a Caulfeild creation, and in part a Telford design.

The section of the A82 illustrated here, which runs from Crainlarich to Fort William, was largely constructed by Caulfeild between 1749 and 1750. From the bleak Rannoch Moor the road climbs to its highest point of 348 m (1,142 ft) near Beinn Chaorach.

The section shown on the map with a viewpoint sits at the top of the Devil's Staircase, allegedly named by the soldiers building the road who had to carry their materials up its zig-zag bends. The road-construction exercise was so perilous that the devil sometimes 'claimed his own'. Looking out over the incredible views of Ben Nevis and Glen Coe makes this route one of the most breathtaking in Scotland.

MAP 09

1. Wade's original Military Route linked three forts: Fort Augustus at Loch Ness, Fort George at Inverness, and which other?

2. Which famous long-distance walking path passes through this road?

3. What event – commemorated at the Glencoe visitor centre – took place in 1692 as a result of Clan MacDonald not pledging an oath of allegiance to William and Mary?

4. Which waterfall with a 120 m drop can be found in the dramatic Nevis Gorge?

5. Wade established encampments at ten-mile intervals along his routes. The inns that developed there became known as Kingshouses. On which moor can you see one such famous inn?

6. Glencoe National Nature Reserve was used as the location for which James Bond film?

7. 'Munro' is the name given to a mountain in Scotland that is 3,000 ft (943 m) or higher. Which is the highest Munro?

8. Sgorr Dhonuill + Stob Ban – Sgurr-Finnisg-Aig – Beinn Molurgainn = which Munro?

9. Which glen is an anagram of TEARS?

10. What Günter Grass wrote about, broadcast.

Opposite: Extract from *The AA Great Britain Road Atlas 2020* (2019). Although the original map is 1:200,000 scale, it has been scaled down in this reproduction to fit.

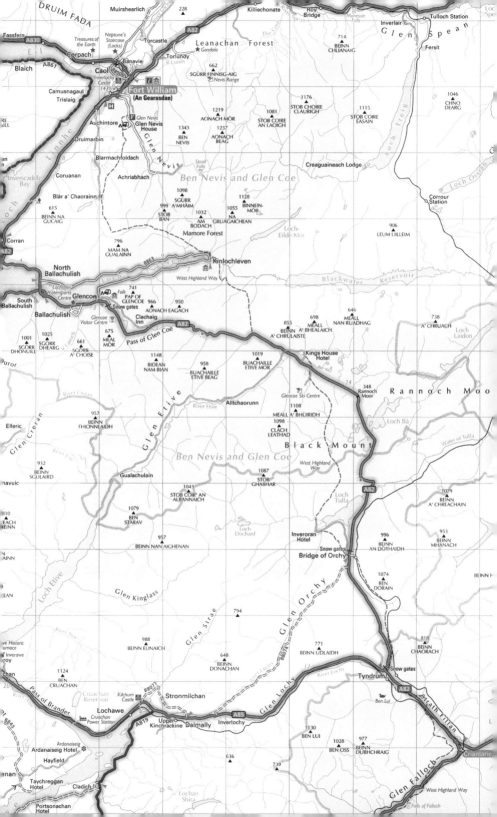

"

...the said Kingdoms of Great Britain and Ireland shall, upon the first Day of January which shall be in the Year of our Lord one thousand eight hundred and one, and for ever after, be united into one Kingdom, by the Name of The United Kingdom of Great Britain and Ireland . . .

The Union with Ireland Act 1800

"

THE COLOSSUS OF ROADS
A5

The Act of Union between Great Britain and Ireland in 1800 created an urgency for faster communications between London and Dublin. Scottish engineer Thomas Telford was tasked with rebuilding the old London to Holyhead road, as Holyhead was one of the main ports for ferries to Dublin. Much of this road – the modern A5 – followed the old Roman route of Watling Street (*see Puzzle 2*), which ran northwest from London as far as Wroxeter. But it was the Welsh section of road that truly tested Telford's engineering skills.

The section beyond Llangollen had to be constructed from scratch, and the road deviated from the original Roman route between Capel Curig and Bethesda.

Telford had to find a way to cross the Menai Strait, a narrow stretch of water separating Anglesey island from mainland Wales. He answered the challenge with his Menai Suspension Bridge (Pont Grog y Borth), started in 1819 and completed in 1826, and today Grade 1 listed. Made from wrought iron, it spans 417 metres, bridging the strait between Bangor and Anglesey.

MAP 10

1. Where does Telford's Waterloo Bridge cross the River Conwy?

2. What other famous suspension bridge, designed by Telford and now in the care of the National Trust, can be seen on this map?

3. Which poet nicknamed Thomas Telford 'the Colossus of Roads'?

4. THE BEADS is an anagram of which place on this stretch of the A5?

5. How many narrow-gauge railways are shown on the map?

6. Which five of Edward's Iron Ring of castles are shown on the map?

7. Given the scale of this map, which is 10 miles to one grid square, estimate to the nearest five minutes how long it would take you to get from Holyhead to Capel Curig travelling on the A5 road at an average speed of 40 mph.

8. Barclodiad y Gawres and Bryn-Celli-Ddu, shown on the map, are both what?

9. Where the old road had gradients of one in six (16.6%), Telford's new road had no gradients greater than one in 17 (6%). If you travelled 5 miles up a hill with a gradient of 6%, what would be your elevation gain in feet? (*Hint*: there are 5280 feet in a mile.)

10. Concerned with small horse outside entrance to hotel.

Opposite: Extract from *The AA Junior Atlas of Britain* (1983), at a scale of 1:500,000.

About the map

The arrival of the motorways revived the idea of the old strip map. This example from *The AA Complete Atlas of Britain* (1979) simplified the navigation of the motorways for its members.

SCOTCH CORNER
A1(M)

The Scotch Corner junction has been made famous by its importance as a staging post throughout road history. Seen by many as a gateway to the true north, it is the place where traffic from London, the M6 in the north west (via the A66) and Yorkshire (A6108) converge to head north towards Scotland – hence Scotch Corner. In Roman times, it was where Dere Street (the continuation of Ermine Street) crossed a road running to Bowes in Durham and Brough in Yorkshire.

The Romans took control of the north in the first century at the Battle of Scotch Corner, and later, in the fourteenth century, the Battle of Old Byland was fought here in the Wars of Scottish Independence.

The Three Tuns Inn, which once stood at Scotch Corner, was a famous Georgian coaching inn on the Great North Road (*see Puzzle 5*). Today the huge Scotch Corner Hotel looms large, along with Moto Services.

Despite being numbered the first motorway, the M1 was not the first stretch of motorway to be opened. That title belongs to the Preston bypass (*see Puzzle 35*). It was, however, Britain's first full-length motorway, and opened a year later, in 1959. Like most of our roads, it was a work in progress, growing new stretches over time. In 1977 the southern end was extended and in 1999 the northern end was extended from Leeds to meet the A1(M).

MAP 11

1. Given the toll fare at the Tyne Tunnel was £1.80 in 2019, and this map was printed in 1979, what has been the average annual percentage increase?

2. What is the distance to Spennymore from the A1(M) junction?

3. What connects mine, band and gates?

4. Which place gets its name from a Roman fort and the road that ran through it?

5. Which place is an anagram of LIBERTY?

6. What type of junction is depicted at D?

7. What is the distance from C to G?

8. Travelling south, how would the exit be signed for Sedgefield?

9. Which place gets its name from a little old well in the north of Durham?

10. Grace, perhaps, getting a century.

Opposite: See p.62 for details of the map.

SCOTCH CORNER–TYNESIDE

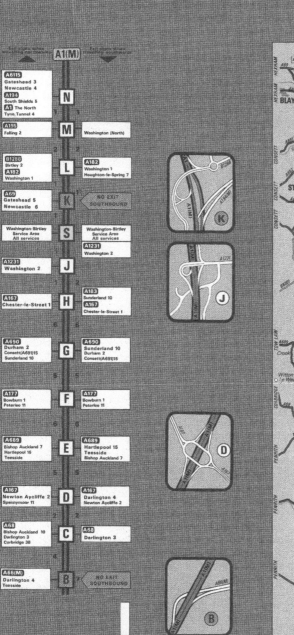

Exit signs when travelling northbound · Exit signs when travelling southbound

A1(M)

Northbound	Jct	Southbound
A6115 Gateshead 3, Newcastle 4 / **A194** South Shields 5, **A1** The North, Tyne, Tunnel 4	N	
A195 Felling 2	M	Washington (North)
B1288 Birtley 2 / **A182** Washington 1	L	**A182** Washington 1, Houghton-le-Spring 7
A69 Gateshead 5, Newcastle 6	K	NO EXIT SOUTHBOUND
Washington-Birtley Service Area All services	S	Washington-Birtley Service Area All services / **A1231** Washington 2
A1231 Washington 2	J	
A167 Chester-le-Street 1	H	**A183** Sunderland 10 / **A167** Chester-le-Street 1
A690 Durham 2, Consett(A691)15, Sunderland 10	G	**A690** Sunderland 10, Durham 2, Consett(A691)15
A177 Bowburn 1, Peterlee 11	F	**A177** Bowburn 1, Peterlee 11
A689 Bishop Auckland 7, Hartlepool 15, Teesside	E	**A689** Hartlepool 15, Teesside, Bishop Auckland 7
A167 Newton Aycliffe 2, Spennymoor 11	D	**A167** Darlington 4, Newton Aycliffe 2
A68 Bishop Auckland 10, Darlington 3, Corbridge 38	C	**A68** Darlington 3
A66(M) Darlington 4, Teesside	B	NO EXIT SOUTHBOUND

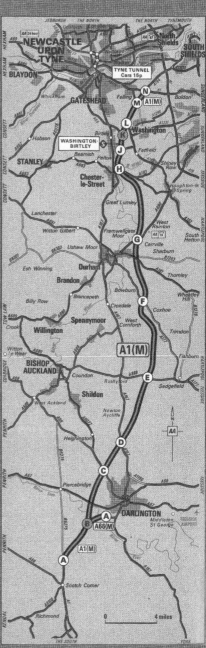

ULTIMATE TEST DRIVES

This next section of puzzles and quizzes offers the perfect test of your driving skills. Or perhaps you want to put your car through its paces. Either way, here are some of the sharpest bends, steepest climbs, blindest summits and trickiest roads to drive in Britain.

It's no wonder that these roads have had a poor safety record, and speed restrictions and extra signage have often been required to improve safety. Experienced drivers are better able to judge the appropriate speed before entering a tight corner. Drivers should avoid braking while on a bend, particularly in bad weather when the car is more likely to lose traction. Harsh braking puts heavy load through the front tyres, which are already dealing with centrifugal force from the corner, and this can result in the driver losing control of the car. As you come out of the bend you can begin to accelerate again.

Limit point analysis can help drivers judge their speed around corners. The limit point is the point where you can no longer see the road ahead. When you reach a sharp bend, you don't know what is beyond your limit point, so you need to adjust your speed to give yourself sufficient response time.

The AA owns the UK's two largest driving schools: AA Driving School, which was launched in 1992, and the British School of Motoring (BSM), which was founded in 1910 and taught Queen Elizabeth II to drive.

DriveTech is also part of the AA and supports UK police forces by providing driver education to people who have committed road offences and helping to make them better, safer drivers.

Opposite: A panoramic view of Cheddar Gorge / Photo by David Iliff / CC BY-SA 3.0.

Rule 166

*DO NOT overtake if there is any doubt, or where
you cannot see far enough ahead to be sure it is safe.
For example, when you are approaching*

- *a corner or bend*

- *a hump bridge*

- *the brow of a hill.*

The Highway Code

SNAKE PASS
A57

This hill pass in the Peak District takes the A57 through the rugged, wild open space of the High Peak Moors to create the shortest route between Manchester and Sheffield. The road was engineered by Thomas Telford (*see Puzzle 10*) and opened in 1821. It was the highest turnpike road in England and offered excellent views over Manchester.

The Sheffield to Glossop Turnpike stopped collecting tolls on the route in 1870, and since the 1980s, the alternative route between Manchester and Sheffield via Woodhead Pass has become more popular as it connects directly with the M1. The Snake Pass route across the Pennines has never been replaced by motorway, despite joining two large cities. This is predominantly because of the cost and difficulty of constructing a highway through the Peak District.

The road is a popular 5 km hill climb with cyclists, with its average gradient of approximately 7%.

MAP 12

1. Which Sheffield band included a song entitled 'The Snake' on their 2001 album *Secrets*, referencing this road?

2. Which conservation charity controls the High Peak Estate which the route cuts through?

3. Which place shares its name with Tuppy, Honoria and Sir Roderick from P.G. Wodehouse's *Jeeves & Wooster* stories?

4. What is the link between ---- Holes, -------pit, ----sworth?

5. Which place is home to the Derbyshire and Lancashire Gliding Club?

6. What ornamental mineral stone is mined at Treak Cliff Cavern and Blue John Caverns?

7. Which place is an anagram of YARD BELOW?

8. Starting from Edale, which is the first place you would reach on the Pennine Way after about 16 miles?

9. Cattle call, resonating loudly and clearly.

10. He'd be prepared to be nicer?

Opposite: Extract from *The AA Great Britain Road Atlas* (1987) at a scale of 1:200,000.

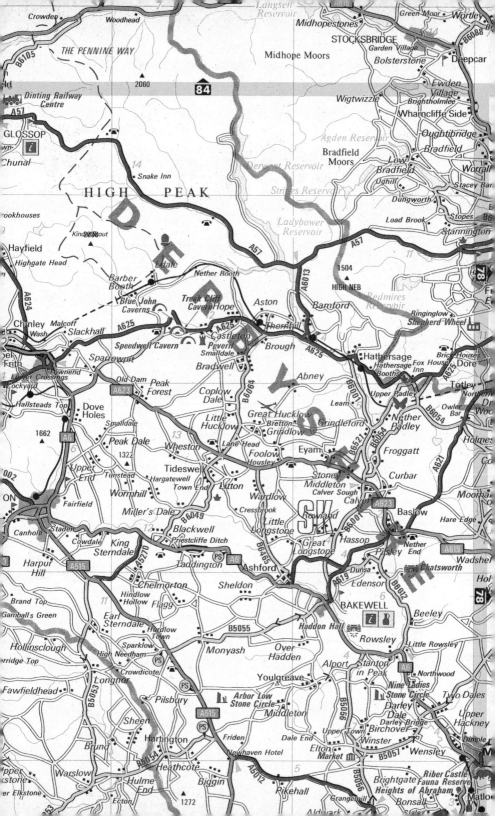

Mapping milestone

In 2006, The AA became the first publisher in Britain to highlight the locations of all fixed speed cameras in our atlases. This move was in keeping with our history – The AA was founded in 1905 to warn drivers of police speed traps.

EVO TRIANGLE
A543 and A5

The British motoring magazine, *Evo*, which focuses on sports and performance cars, conceived this triangular route to test drive cars. The 20-mile route along the A543 and A5 celebrates the thrill of driving and provides the perfect challenge for both car and driver.

The route links Pentrefoelas and Cerrigydrudion near Denbigh Moors. Offering some incredible scenery through Snowdonia and views of the Llyn Brenig Lake, the triangle has some tight and sweeping bends.

Has the road attracted dangerous drivers? A recent campaign to improve safety on this road resulted in a government grant of half a million pounds to install average speed cameras on the A543 in 2019. For some, this has all but taken away the romance of this route, but it's been argued that the popularisation of the triangle meant that motorists were using it like a racetrack, and the road had seen four fatalities since 2012.

MAP 13

1. The map shows the boundaries between which three Welsh county boroughs (unitary authority areas)?

2. What man-made feature, with a nine-mile perimeter, sits on the border between Conwy and Denbighshire?

3. Which place on the triangle is an anagram of IRONIC DRUDGERY?

4. What is the sum of the road numbers on this map (each road only being used once)?

5. What is the Welsh name for a river?

6. If the *Evo* triangle is isosceles, with two sides of 8 miles and a base of 5 miles, what is its area, rounded to the nearest square mile?

7. What does the Welsh 'cwm' mean in English?

8. Using a cypher where a = 1, b = 2, c = 3 etc, and then adding the numbers together, how much is Hafod-Dinbych?

9. Where might you find a large stone (Ring Cairn) marking the site of a Mesolithic camp?

10. Dodgy slang used about cook?

Opposite: Extract from *AA Close-Up Britain Atlas, 2nd edition* (2008). The map is at a scale of 1:100,000.

The Black Mountains
[Welsh: Y Mynydd Du]

noun

No one knows exactly why they are called the Black Mountains – presumably it's due to their overshadowing size and darkness in poor weather. But they were known as 'Blak Montyne' in the fifteenth century and 'Black-mountaine' a hundred years later, before becoming 'Black Mountains' in the nineteenth century. Carreg means 'stone' or 'rock' in Welsh.

BLACK MOUNTAIN ROAD
A4069

This hill pass through the Brecon Beacons National Park connects Llandovery to Ystradgynlais. Peaking at 493 m (1,617 ft) above sea level, the road offers unparalleled views of the Black Mountains, if you can stop in one of the lay-bys. But the endless switchbacks and the lack of guardrails mean that if you're in the driving seat, you'll need all of your focus on the road.

When you're not sharing the road with roaming sheep you might meet other driving enthusiasts: it's been known as the '*Top Gear* road' since Jeremy Clarkson was filmed driving it in 2011.

The 20-mile (32-km) stretch of road is best driven from north to south. It starts at the junction with the A40 at Llandovery, goes on through Llangadog, and crosses the Black Mountains, including the hairpin bend known as Tro Gwcw ('cuckoo turn'). Stop and enjoy views of the Tywi valley before passing through Lower Brynammon and reaching the junction with the A474 at Gwaun-Cae-Gurwen.

MAP 14

1. For what purpose was limestone mined here?

2. Which spectacularly situated stronghold lies a few miles west of the Black Mountain Road?

3. What is the highest peak on the map?

4. Guided by a star to this location?

5. White Canons would have worshipped here.

6. Which ridge hill sits 4.5 miles southeast of Llandovery?

7. Which place is an anagram of TOWN PARADE?

8. Which village in the heart of the coalfield shares its name with places in East Sussex and North London?

9. The boundary between which two counties dissects the Usk Reservoir?

10. Friend losing head touring Hampshire town.

Opposite: Extract from *The AA Great Britain Road Atlas 2020* (2019) at a scale of 1:200,000.

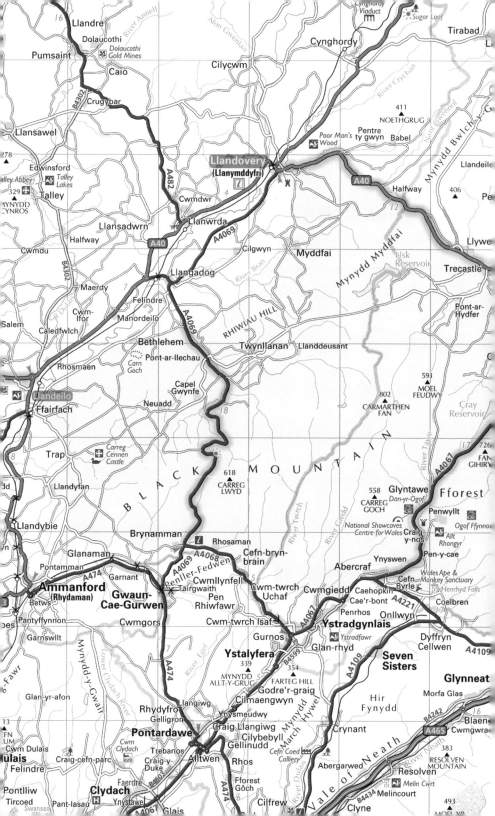

gorge /gɔːdʒ/

noun

A narrow valley between hills or mountains, typically with steep rocky walls and a stream running through it.

The word originates from the mid-eighteenth century and originally meant 'throat', from the Old French 'gorge'.

CHEDDAR GORGE
B3135

Cliff Road takes you through the scenic section of Somerset's Mendip Hills. The road leaves Cheddar in a series of tight twists through the cliff faces of the gorge as you travel nearly 9 miles east towards Green Ore.

Cheddar Gorge is England's deepest natural canyon, its cliffs reaching 138 m (453 ft) above the road at points. At its maximum, the gradient of the road reaches 16%, making it a steep climb, and requiring the road to be sometimes shut in bad weather.

Leaving the gorge, you climb steeply between the cliffs and around the famous Horseshoe bend. Both the landscape and road begin to change as you come out of the gorge after Black Rock Gate, with bends becoming longer and more sweeping, and gradually allowing some opportunities for overtaking.

The B3135 reaches the Medip Plateau and then forks at the junction where it meets the B3371. Along Plummer's Lane, the road opens up and takes you on to Green Ore where it meets the A39, which takes you northeast to Chewton Mendip or southwest to Wells. The road carries on beyond Green Ore until it reaches the A37 a further 3 miles east.

MAP 15

1.   A legendary witch resided here.

2.   Which rock type, carved out by glacial meltwater, forms the steep cliffs of Cheddar Gorge?

3.   The Cheddar caves offer the perfect humidity and steady temperature to make Cheddar cheese, but does Cheddar cheese have a protected designation of origin?

4.   Given the scale of the map is 1:100,000, what is the distance between Cheddar Gorge and Chewton Mendip as the crow flies?

5.   If you drove for a quarter of a kilometre along the B3135 at its steepest gradient, what would be your elevation gain in metres?

6.   Which place is an anagram of ATONES?

7.   Which place is named after the river it bridges?

8.   Which place contains a pair of homonyms in its name?

9.   Water flows here from the Cheddar Yeo river in Cheddar Gorge.

10.   Map maker's place?

Opposite: Extract from *The AA Close-Up Britain Atlas, 2nd edition* (2008), which uses a scale of 1:100,000.

Rule 146

Adapt your driving *to the appropriate type and condition of road you are on. In particular*

- *do not treat speed limits as a target. It is often not appropriate or safe to drive at the maximum speed limit*

- *take the road and traffic conditions into account. Be prepared for unexpected or difficult situations, for example, the road being blocked beyond a blind bend. Be prepared to adjust your speed as a precaution . . .*

The Highway Code

CAT AND FIDDLE ROAD
A537

Running between Macclesfield and Buxton in the Peak District, this road gets its name from the Cat and Fiddle Inn that has sat at its summit since opening in 1813. Outside, it has an OS elevation marker showing it to be 515 m (1,689 ft) above sea level. This makes it the second-highest pub in Britain after the Tan Hill Inn on the Pennine Way.

An AA survey in 2003 named this 7.5-mile stretch of road in Cheshire as the most dangerous in the UK. Its many sharp corners can defeat unwary drivers, and there were forty-four serious or fatal crashes on the road between 2007 and 2011.

The road is particularly popular with bikers looking for a technical challenge. Motorcyclists have represented 2% of its usage but 75% of its most serious accidents. To reduce accidents, a 50 mph speed restriction and speed cameras have been put in place.

Stop along this twisty road with its dry-stone-wall edging and you can take in incredible views of Greater Manchester, the Cheshire Plain and the Peak District National Park.

MAP 16

1. Who laughed in the nursery rhyme featuring a cat and fiddle?

2. The Cat and Fiddle road is part of a triangle of roads beloved by drivers and cyclists seeking a challenge. If the B5470 is the second side, can you name the third?

3. What is the sum of the three roads that form the Cat and Fiddle route?

4. Which river is a tributary of the River Mersey?

5. Which small town takes its name from the Anglo-Saxon 'weg leah', which means 'a clearing by the road'?

6. The Cheshire–Derbyshire border runs along the line of which river on the map?

7. Which town, famous for its cotton, sits on the Macclesfield Canal?

8. Sounds like a police patrol.

9. The National Trust estate with the lake where Mr Darcy met Miss Bennet in the BBC's adaptation of *Pride and Prejudice*.

10. Travelling back and forth not quick, it's said.

Opposite: Extract from *The AA Close-Up Britain Atlas, 2nd edition* (2008), which uses a scale of 1:100,000.

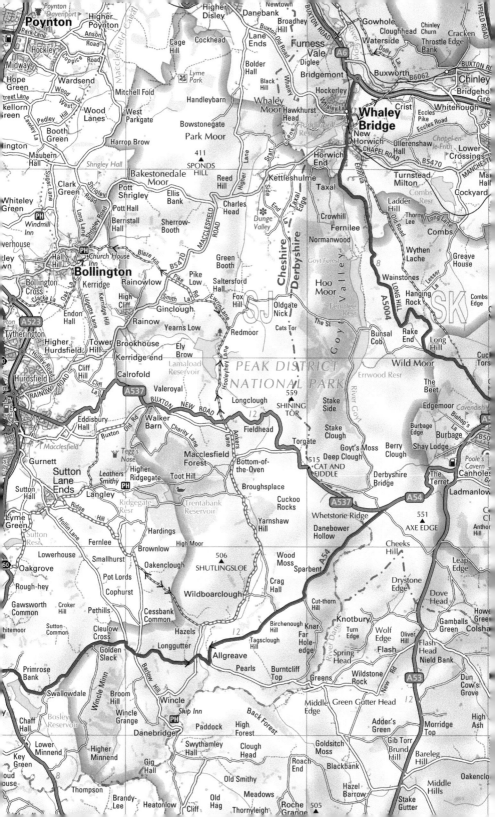

Buttermere /ˈbʌtəˌmɪə/

noun

The name Buttermere is probably derived from the Old Norse name 'Buthar', as in 'Buthar's lake'. It is said that an eleventh-century Viking called Buthar or Boethar controlled the area of Buttermere, and this explanation seems likely given the other Norse names in the area.

HONISTER PASS
B5289

This mountain pass in the Lake District links Seatoller, in the east of the Borrowdale valley, to Gatesgarth Farm at the southern end of Buttermere. For centuries, pack ponies offered the only means of transporting goods between villages and towns across the Lake District. Honister Pass is one such packhorse route, used for over three hundred years to transport slate from the Honister quarries across the peaks to the coast near Ravenglass. The farm at the valley-head would have been an important staging post for the ponies.

The pass holds the 24-hour rainfall record in the UK, with 341.1 mm of rain falling on 5 December 2015. Even in less extreme weather, the route would often have been dangerous: the road is steep, with a gradient of 1 in 4 (25%). As you can see in the map extract, Honister Pass is one of Cumbria's highest passes, with a summit height of 356 m (1,168 feet).

MAP 17

1. What links Ros, Stone and Sea?

2. It would take you a long time to find a needle here.

3. What is the sum of the Greats minus the sum of the Pikes?

4. Which three islands are depicted on the map?

5. Complete Robert Southey's poem 'How does the water come down at ------'?

6. What is the saddle between two hills?

7. Buttermere sits at one end of the Honister Pass. What is a 'mere'?

8. What do the two black opposing arrows on the road between Buttermere and Newlands indicate?

9. Which other hill pass can be seen on this map, and what can tourists find there?

10. The irons to be replaced.

Opposite: Extract from *The AA Close-Up Britain Atlas, 2nd edition* (2008), which uses a scale of 1:100,000.

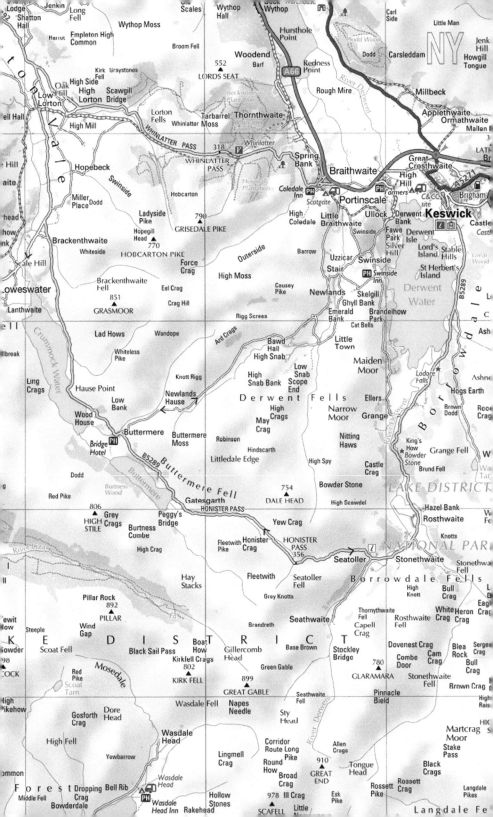

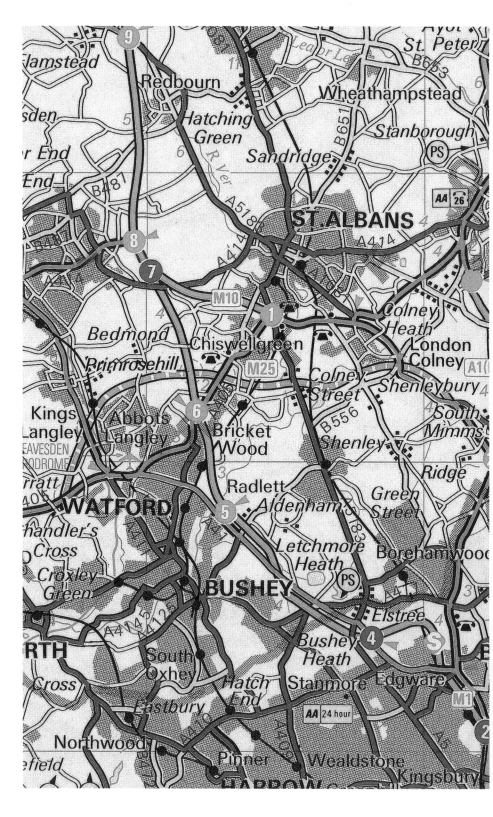

RING ROADS AND BYPASSES

As traffic volumes grew steadily through the twentieth century, and the golden age of motoring turned into gridlock, solutions were sought to relieve congestion and improve traffic flow. But building new roads in Britain, particularly around its most densely populated urban areas, is a controversial business.

Following World War I, transport plans such as London's North Circular and Golden Mile were essentially industrial plans. Just as with the earliest roads, trade and war still acted as the main incentives for investment in new infrastructure.

The successive failed attempts to improve the South Circular, and the many years it took for the M25 to be built, illustrate the difficulty of such endeavours. Whether it's the loss of homes as a result of the compulsory purchase of housing to make way for new roads, or the risk to our ancient meadows and woodlands, the building of roads attracts objectors on every side. In the 1990s, major protests at the A30 extension in Fairmile in Devon, at Twyford Down over the M3 Winchester bypass, and concerning the A34 bypass at Newbury, all made news headlines.

While the terms ring road and orbital – and loop roads in the United States – are virtually synonymous, 'orbital' tends to be used for motorway-grade roads. London's Inner Ring Road marks the boundary for the congestion charge zone and divides Central London and Outer London. The M25 has become a geographical marker, encompassing nearly all of Greater London, and influencing house-building and home-buying alike.

Opposite: The AA Motorists Atlas from 1985 shows the evolving M25.

Mapping milestone

In 1984 we fully computerised the Home Routes
Service, and three years later had fully computerised
the Overseas Routes Service.

THE LONDON ORBITAL
M25

As traffic continued to grow in London through the early twentieth century, Sir Charles Bressey and Sir Edwin Lutyens were commissioned to produce a Highway Development Survey in 1937, with plans and recommendations to ease congestion. One of their proposals was for a series of orbital roads. The war, and post-war austerity, meant these ideas were shelved.

By the 1960s traffic had grown even heavier, and the Greater London Council returned to their idea and proposed a similar series of four ring roads around the capital: the London Ringways plan. Ringway 2 consisted of an upgrade to the North Circular, and a few other sections were started that were later integrated into the M25. The cost and disruption to the capital resulted in huge opposition and eventually the project was cancelled.

In 1975 work began at last on the ambitious M25 plan to create a single outer ring road around Greater London. It opened in October 1986 and at 117 miles (188 km) long it became Europe's second-longest orbital road (after the Berliner ring at 122 miles (196 km)). The M25 was planned to carry a maximum of 88,000 vehicles a day, but immediately exceeded this volume when it opened, earning itself instant notoriety. It is jokingly referred to as 'Britain's biggest car park'.

About the map

The map chosen is The AA's 1989 sheet map of the M25, published shortly after its opening.
The purple lines indicate where motorists are most likely to suffer traffic hold-ups.

MAP 18

1. Who officially declared the London Orbital 'open for business' on 29 October 1986?

2. Which author's year-long pilgrimage around the M25 became the subject of the work *London Orbital*?

3. Which song and album, released in 1989, was inspired by the frustration of travelling on the M25?

4. At its widest, the M25 has a dual six-lane section. Between which junctions is this section?

5. Which counties does the M25 pass through?

6. Name the two motorway service areas on the M25.

7. In 1993 the M25 was carrying 200,000 vehicles a day and by 2014 this had increased to 263,000 vehicles a day at its busiest points. What was the percentage increase over that period?

8. How many AA high street shops are shown on the map?

9. Why was the Dartford Tunnel renamed the Dartford River Crossing in 1991?

10. Boy, and how much you'd get for him?

Brentford /bɹɛnt fɔːd/

noun

Brentford is an Anglo-Saxon name, 'Brent' meaning 'holy one' and 'ford' being the place where the road crossed the River Brent.

THE GOLDEN MILE
A4

In 1925 the five-mile section of road known today as the Great West Road was opened. One mile of it – stretching from Syon Lane to the Gunnersbury roundabout – became known as the Golden Mile for the value of the business along it. The new road allowed traffic to bypass Brentford High Street, which had become horribly congested as a result of the growth of industry in the area.

Brentford has become justifiably proud of the Art Deco buildings that sit along this road. Several of the factories belonged to American manufacturers keen to establish a UK base to avoid trade tariffs. The Gillette building (1936–37), designed by Sir Banister Flight Fletcher, sat on the north side of the road, its clock tower becoming a local landmark. It was so imposing that the corner by Syon Lane became known as Gillette Corner.

However, it was the architects Wallis, Gilbert & Partners who were responsible for most of the Art Deco buildings along the road. Their work included the Coty Cosmetics Factory (1932), Westlink House (1929–30), the former building of Pyrene fire extinguishers, Wallis House (1936–42) and the enormous Firestone Tyre Factory (1928). The Firestone factory was tragically demolished just before it could be listed, and the site now houses the West Cross complex. The gates, lamppost piers and railings of the site are all that remain.

MAP 19

1.   Britain's most popular road name.

2.   What type of interchange can be seen at junction 2 of the M4?

3.   Given the scale of the map is 3.6 inches to the mile, estimate the distance that a train would travel between Syon Lane station and Kew Bridge station.

4.   Where could you ride a narrow-gauge railway?

5.   A road in the style of a New England city.

6.   First emperor of the Roman Empire may be nearby.

7.   Micro-climate named after Diana.

8.   Road named after an eminent Victorian naturalist.

9.   Fire-breathing foe may live here.

10.   Not mad, only confused inwardly.

Opposite: Extract from *AA Street by Street Richmond and Kingston-upon-Thames* (2002), shown at a scale of 1:17,500.

Mapping milestone

In 1973 we create The AA Roadwatch traffic service,
due to the arrival of commercial radio in the UK.

THE NORTH CIRCULAR
A406

It was recently reported that the stretch of the North Circular between the Chiswick Roundabout and Hanger Lane was the worst bottleneck in Britain, meaning regular users would lose sixty-one hours a year sitting in traffic jams. It has also won accolades for being Britain's noisiest road and most polluted road.

Conceived in 1910, the North Circular was constructed in the 1920s and 30s as an outer London ring road to link the growing industrial hotspots of London without traffic having to go through the centre of the city. Following World War I, former military and munitions factories along this route were repurposed for manufacturing industry, providing much needed employment. Running 25.7 miles (41.4 km) from Chiswick, it initially ran to Southgate and used existing roads to the east of Southgate. In 1987 the South Woodford to Barking relief road was opened and then, in the 1990s, it was extended as far as Woolwich.

Unlike the South Circular, the roads have been widened over the years at the cost of demolition to local housing, and most of it runs on purpose-built dual carriageway. The uncertainty and upheaval of this constant stream of improvements has taken its toll on its urban surroundings. Now there are a number of proposed regeneration schemes looking to tackle this problem.

MAP 20

1. The North Circular passes through which interchange at its most northerly point?

2. The Brent Cross Shopping Centre sits on which junction of the North Circular?

3. Which famous gyratory system sits on top of the Western Avenue (A40)?

4. Which viaduct was created on the North Circular to allow the road to stand free from a flood plain?

5. Which roundabout shares its name with a character from Snoopy?

6. Why was Britain's first 'hands free' pedestrian crossing installed at the Henlys Corner junction in 2011?

7. String instrument from dragon country.

8. Once home of the Spurs.

9. Institute a republic?

10. Can you find the places listed below in this circular word search?

```
                        P L L
                    C A O H Z E J A E
                B E S G W Z Q B P G X X F
            N D G H I O O I U Q G Z D X A Y K
          Y O G K W T R E D B R I D G E F E Z H
        P R D X N S W G G Y P A I J X K K L B Y M
        H V N E M S G M K I G J L B Q L R H A V T
    J Z N E A K K G J I G V I I P F K Q C R U Q M
    A B O H E B O E M P N Z Q W G E A J N K L X M
  N R V T K Z W I S L I N G T O N E R U I I G G I Y
  D N L C Y U Y O C W N E H Q U M I T T F N A Q C G
  P A O A Q P D K Q K A I I Y A Y Q R R O G W H W J
D W I L L E S D E N I J M G J M U Y S B D N M O O Y A
N D H R B E C K T O N A E H W L P R P R K Z Y U O K O
M O K U U V I J H Z H D W A G C P U B Q D E H H D N T
  R L N L N W P C N X B Q M Q L A B U J L K J K F Z
  E U I D L P R E D M O N T O N I S Y B G S I N O Y
  V Q F U S U T Y S C I L F O R D R M T C H B A R Y
    V R F H T U E O V Y P Z M X F E B X H S G W D
    P C U O B I Z U B D R W A E W N F E J N L K H
      H T W C W X T O H F T Y K S N Z S M Y S Q
      Q U V X G S H N E A S D E N U B U V C T D
        C A Y A A G S D A Q B G C G N I L A E
          P P E N A B N G Q W T P C E F S C
            A U T H H H W G C U P L H V
              E D B A H O S N W
                  V K X
```

Acton	Edmonton	Ilford	Tottenham
Alperton	Finchley	Islington	Walthamstow
Barking	Gunnersbury	Neasden	Wembley
Beckton	Hendon	Redbridge	Willesden
Ealing	Higham	Southgate	Woodford

Next page: Extract from *The AA Close-Up Britain Atlas, 2nd edition* (2008) illustrates the whole circular at a scale of 1:100,000.

"

Around eight of every ten journeys in London are made using our roads – whether by car, taxi, motorbike, bus, cycle, foot or freight – which is why it is vital that we think big. We must deliver long-term solutions that will not just make the most of the space we have for road users but bring environmental and amenity improvements to local areas.

Boris Johnson, unveiling his plans to ease congestion on the South Circular, February 2013

"

THE SOUTH CIRCULAR
A205

Building started on the southern semi-circular road around London in 1921, with a stretch of purpose-built road from Well Hall Road to Eltham Road. Unlike the North Circular, however, the original plan never proceeded much beyond this, and the South Circular has remained a strung-together series of single-carriageway urban roads. In fact, it could be argued that no South Circular road really exists.

Running 20.5 miles (33 km) long, from the Chiswick flyover in the west to the Woolwich ferry in the east, the road retains most of the original road names along its route. It uses the A3 (the old London to Portsmouth road) for two miles between Clapham Common and the end of Wandsworth High Street.

The numerous proposals to improve the road over time have included the 1960s London Ringways Plan, upgrading the South Circular to a motorway as part of 'Ringway 2'; a 1980s plan for a raised dual-carriageway road built over the existing railway lines; and in 2013 Boris Johnson's plan for a series of underground tunnels.

The puzzle questions that follow are based on the map of the South Circular shown on pages 108–9.

MAP 21

1.   Which 'commons' does the South Circular pass through?

2.   Which historic greyhound racing stadium sits on the South Circular road?

3.   What is a grade-separated junction and how many exist on the route?

4.   The South Circular is assigned as a London 'red route'. What does this prevent traffic from doing?

5.   Stop off for a pint on this route at a popular Dutch building with sails.

6.   Home of Charlton Athletic FC.

7.   Old monastery between Richmond Park and the Thames.

8.   Once the home of a Victorian Scottish author.

9.   Adverse reaction to cardigan maybe being picked up.

Pages 108-9: Extract from *The AA Close-Up Britain Atlas, 2nd edition* (2008) illustrating the South and North Circulars at a scale of 1:100,000.

10. Can you find the places listed below
in this circular word search?

```
                        Z F F
                      K C Z G Q D K J Q
                  Q R N F P E C X F B D G U
              G K E M Q Q Y Q J Z J D H L X D S
          N A O S L R F S M U V Z Y L V O U R R
      W U S O O O O T A P J V F X K R B V I H R
      Q J Y W I J R H P C R Z D E K A L T R O M
  J N Q D R U E L N A M Q J H C I W L U D Q Z T
  G T K E I A A H E H M E S U B Y X K L C Z U E
E M A Y N T B X R I C H M O N D M C B C T K S L R
O C W K H L A Z Q T N J M Y X Q A O W X M J N N N
Z F Q A A E T X T O W D A X X F H L N M H S P B V
W B B M X M D X D T H S S H X K N P D P P W B L L G B
O L L D U U P R P Q O A M T F E Z A H N O C T T R U T
W Y U T A C P M O R P H Q L K V E L A W O O L W I C H
  A P U L W A J Y F G B Y E L M V C R T H E D J O M
  E N B Q H N B X Q T U W E C B Z X B Q C H M D M Y
  D F D E H E D W K K A S E N R A B O I V A H P C B
    L O S H W N F C P R C Y J T X X U G B R L H D
    R X E W X T O I O C F L W U U W R L T A N L W
      O O D O G F W J I T A B G O P E R G N O I
      G O A Y R U S N O T X I R B W R V A C X T
        M V B M T I C F M A I Q I C A D N W B
          S O U T H F I E L D S V M S L L L
            P L C V J R E H O V I D I
              L F I I A W T L B
                M X G
```

Balham	Clapham	Lewisham	Southfields
Barnes	Coldharbour	Mortlake	Streatham
Brixton	Dulwich	Putney	Sydenham
Catford	Eltham	Richmond	Wandsworth
Chiswick	Kew	Roehampton	Woolwich

We take great care when we decide to build a new road and we avoid sensitive sites whenever we can. I intend to inspect proposals very carefully to ensure that all realistic options are exhausted before we tread on Sites of Special Scientific Interest in future.

Dr Brian Mawhinney, Secretary of State for Transport, 27 February 1995

THE NEWBURY BYPASS
A34

Look at the map, and you will immediately see that there are not one, but two Newbury bypasses. The first one, built in 1963, was simply unable to carry the amount of traffic that flooded the Newbury area by the 1980s. The route of the new proposed bypass was highly controversial, given it would run through the North West Downs (designated an Area of Outstanding Natural Beauty), The Chase (a National Trust nature reserve) and the site of the first Battle of Newbury (an English Heritage site).

In July 1995, the Secretary of State for Transport, Brian Mawhinney, gave the go-ahead for the building of the road and then resigned just half an hour later. The map extract from *The AA Great Britain Road Atlas 13th edition* (1998) shows the bypass under construction.

The protest against the bypass became known as the 'Third Battle of Newbury', a reference to the two English Civil War battles that had taken place nearby. Protesters created makeshift tree house camps, tree sitting in Snelsmore Common. A second group settled at the River Kennet, alongside the Kennet and Avon Canal, and a few months later there were twenty protest encampments along the route. In February 1996 there was a two-mile protest march along the route attended by five thousand people: the largest-recorded road-building demonstration in Britain.

MAP 22

1. The proposed bypass route was home to a rare species of snail: true or false?

2. Which famous environmentalist and broadcaster opposed the bypass?

3. Which iconic road protester of the 1990s was originally from Newbury?

4. Which junction of the M4 is known as the 'Newbury Junction' or 'Chieveley Interchange'?

5. Given that 50 mm on the map represents 10 km, approximate the distance from the AA shop in Basingstoke to the centre of Andover as the crow flies?

6. Where can you find paintings of World War I by English artist Stanley Spencer?

7. What is the link between hay, cott and mancott?

8. Location for *Downton Abbey*?

9. Can you find five Ends?

10. Had a dress on backwards, around November, and again later.

Opposite: Extract from *The AA Great Britain Road Atlas, 13th edition* (1998), using a scale of 1:200,000.

South Rawley · Brightwalton · Lilley · Stanmore · Compton · Four Points · Basildon · Harbour · Child Beale

Chaddleworth · Brightwalton Green · Brightwalton Holt · Mell Green · Beedon · Beedon Hill · Ashampstead Green · Quick's Green · Basildon Park NT · A329

Great Shefford · Leckhampstead Thicket · Peasemore · World's End · Bothampstead · Ashampstead · Hampstead Norrey's · Upper Basildon · Pangbourne · A340 · 7 · Tidmarsh

Weston · Welford · Leckhampstead · Downend · Royal County of Berkshire · Yattendon · Burnt Hill · M4 · 12

East Shefford · 36 · Chieveley · Hermitage · Little Hungerford · Frilsham · Bradfield · Englefield · Nor St · Theale

Wickham Green · Winterbourne · 13 · Newbury · Wellhouse · Stanford Dingley · Chapel Row · Sulhamstead · Tras

Westbrook · Easton · Boxford · Curridge · Cold Ash · Bucklebury · Upper Bucklebury · Beenham · A4

Wickham · Halfway · Wickham Heath · Stockcross · Donnington · Shaw · Thatcham · Midgham · Woolhampton · Padworth · Aldermaston · Ufton Nervet

Jarvis Elcot Park · Elcot · Newbury · Skinners Green · Speen · R Kennet · Brimpton · Wasing · Pamber Heath

Hell Corner · Hamstead Marshall · Enborne · Enborne Row · Newtown · Greenham · Goldfinch Bottom · Crookham · Headley · Ashford Hill · Heath End · Tadley · Baughurst · Pamber Green · Silche

West Woodhay · Ball Hill · Broad Laying · Bishop's Green · Brock's Green · Plastow Green · Browninghill Green · West Heath · Charter Alley · Little London · Pamber End

Woolton Hill · Heath End · East Woodhay · Penwood · Burghclere · Wolverton Common · Towns End · Monk Sherborne · Sherbor St Jo

Pilot Hill · Highclere · Pound Street · Whitway · Old Burghclere · Kingsclere · Wolverton · Ramsdell · The Vyne NT

Faccombe · Ashmansworth · Highclere Castle · Sydmonton · A339 · 12

Crux Easton · Beacon Hill · Ladle Hill (unfinished hill fort) · Cottington's Hill · Hannington · Upper Wootton

Binley · Woodcott · Dunley · Litchfield · North Oakley · Ibworth · Wootton St Lawrence · Worting · BASINGSTOKE · AA

Stoke · Egbury · Cole Henley · Quidhampton · Newfound · Clarken Green · Deane · Oakley · Kempshott · A3010

Swampton · St Mary Bourne · Freefolk · Southington · Ashe · East Oakley · A30 · M3

Little London · Smannell · Overton · Laverstoke · Steventon · 7 · Dummer · Farleigh Wallop · Ellisfield

Picket Piece · Tinker's Hill · Hurstbourne Priors · Tufton · Silk Mill · Whitchurch · North Waltham · 8 · Popham · Woodmancott · Nutley · Axford

Andover · Longparish · East Aston · Middleton · A303 · Micheldever Station · Preston Candover · Chilton Candover · Bra

Clatford · Cottage End · Forton · Bransbury · West Stratton · Chilton Candover · Lower Wield

Wherwell · Newton Stacey · Bullington · Hunton · Weston Colley · Northbrook · East Stratton · Upper Wield · Hattingle

Chilbolton · Barton Stacey · Sutton Scotney · Wonston · Stoke Charity · Micheldever · Northington · Brown Candover · Swarraton

Leckford · Crawley · B3420 · A34 · A33 · M3

"

*The fact is that we have an old centre through which
we are trying to drive our modern tramcars and so on,
and we find that it is impossible to do it. We have to cut
and carve and rearrange things. If we intend to develop
the outskirts of our towns simply to suit the conditions
of the present day, surely we are likely to be . . . in 50 or
100 years faced with a series of problems which will
be just as difficult of solution then as our
present ones are for us.*

Councillor Marr of the Manchester City Council,
speaking at a conference in 1910

"

HIGHWAY IN THE SKY
A57(M)

At just two miles long, the Mancunian Way is one of the shortest stretches of motorway in the country. Together with the A6042 Trinity Way and A665 Great Ancoats Street, it forms the Manchester and Salford Inner Ring Road.

Aside from its claim to fame as Britain's third-shortest stretch of motorway, it was also conceived as Britain's first major elevated highway outside of London. The Hammersmith flyover, built using reinforced concrete, had opened in 1961, and the same firm of engineers, Guy Maunsell & Partners, were responsible for both constructions. On its opening in May 1967, the *Manchester Evening News* dubbed it the 'highway in the sky'.

Since the new flyover to the west of the A57(M) was built in 1992, the Mancunian Way has officially comprised both the A57(M) and the A635(M). The A635 got its new secret motorway status in 1995, and although it does not appear on any signs as A635(M) – nor indeed on the map that follows – it is Britain's second-shortest motorway.

MAP 23

1. In which TV drama does the central character awaken to find himself in the 1970s next to a billboard advertising the 'Highway in the Sky'?

2. The Mancunian Way passes through the centre of which university campuses?

3. Which mainline railway stations can you see on the map?

4. What service links Cornbook with St Peter's Square, Market Street and Shudehill?

5. Which place is an anagram of DOLLARS?

6. Former home of *Coronation Street*.

7. What forms the boundary between Manchester and Salford on this map?

8. Road named after an interim ruler.

9. Sum of the roads that make up the Manchester orbital.

10. Drinking's something pleasant, we hear.

Opposite: Extract from *AA Street by Street Greater Manchester (2003)*, using a scale of 1:17,500 or 3.6 inches to 1 mile.

THE
AUTOMOBILE ASSOCIATION
TOURING MAP OF
ENGLAND & WALES

TWELVE MILES TO AN INCH

*Issued exclusively to Members
by the Automobile Association
Fanum House, New Coventry St London W.I.*

PUBLISHED BY
JOHN BARTHOLOMEW & SON, L^{TD}
The Geographical Institute, EDINBURGH

TRUNK ROADS AND TOURING ROUTES

Think of any long-distance journey you've recently undertaken and, in all likelihood, you'll associate it with one of the major trunk roads of Britain. These strategic roads share long histories and holiday memories. The title of Tom Fort's book, *The A303: Highway to the Sun*, summarises their promise. They are roads to freedom, roads to adventure, but only very rarely in Britain, roads to the sun.

In recent years, the marketing of specific driving routes has been seen as a good way to stimulate the economy in areas which rely heavily on tourism. The Atlantic Highway was Devon and Cornwall's answer to Route 66, and in the last few years the same idea has been repeated in Scotland to great success, and on the west coast of Ireland with the Wild Atlantic Way.

Scotland's South West Coastal 300 (or SWC300) follows the precedent set by the North Coast 500 (NC500), a route designed a few years earlier. That route takes a circle from Inverness on the east coast to Applecross on the west, and from Applecross snakes its way around the coast to Durness, across to John O'Groats and back to Inverness. Another route, the North East 250 (NE250) circles around the east coast, going north from Aberdeen, and turns back inland at Buckie, dropping down into the Cairngorms to Braemar and then back to Aberdeen in the east.

Opposite: An interwar touring map from The AA and Bartholomews – touring had become a popular pastime and there was a ready market for a new kind of mapping.

17.2 For the purpose of advances for the construction, improvement, or maintenance of roads, the Minister may, after consultation with the Roads Committee hereinafter referred to and the local authorities affected, classify roads in such manner as he thinks fit . . .

Ministry of Transport Act, 1919

THE A303

The 'New Direct Road' from London to Exeter was proposed in the nineteenth century as a faster coaching route than the A30. William Hanning, chief engineer of the Ilminster Turnpike Trust designed it, and by 1819 the coaching company known as the Scrippy had begun using the new road. The section around Exeter follows the old Fosse Way (*see Puzzle 3*) and the section around Stonehenge follows the pre-Roman Harrow Way.

The A303 was created in 1933 and the 'New Direct Road' was renamed the 'Alternative London–Exeter route' (the A30 being harder to upgrade). The ninety-three-mile route starts at junction 8 of the M3 near Basingstoke and continues to just north of Honiton, where it joins the A30. Nonetheless, the road didn't receive its trunk road status until 1958, and wasn't widened until the 1960s.

Today most of it is dual carriageway, but some sections are still guaranteed to see traffic congestion, especially on busy Bank Holidays, notably in the Stonehenge area where proposals to create a Stonehenge tunnel to reroute the road have been so controversial. The section west of Ilminster runs over the Blackdown Hills and is still single carriageway.

About the map

This lovely old map extract on the previous page is from
The AA Touring Gazetteer and Atlas of Great Britain (1946),
published twelve years before the A303 was designated
a trunk road. The road itself is not numbered but is
assigned a solid red line as a Ministry of Transport
classified A road. It wasn't until 1969 that Andover
and Amesbury were bypassed, so the A303 in
today's atlases looks rather different.

MAP 24

1. What is 303 expressed in binary?

2. Which counties does the A303 pass through?

3. What alternative route can you take from Ilminster to Exeter?

4. Chalk lowland with Hampshire Downs to the east and Berkshire Downs to the north.

5. Wessex town en route called 'Ivell' by Thomas Hardy.

6. Given the map scale of 12 miles to the inch, estimate the distance from Amesbury to Wincanton.

7. Which Area of Outstanding Natural Beauty does the A303 pass through on the Somerset–Devon border?

8. Between which places on the route is the road at its highest altitude?

9. The River Yeo is a tributary of which river?

10. I left clergyman: I must leave.

Mapping milestone

In 1912 we created the first AA paper routes.
They were personalised itineraries, handwritten on
route cards, giving directions, some printed town
plans and booklets of 'day drives'. By the early 1920s,
our routes consisted of a set of handwritten cards,
each giving details of the route between two different
points. Information about local places of interest was
written on the reverse.

TRUNK ROAD TO THE SEA
A13

Conceived in Georgian times to link the City with the expanding Docklands area, this important route to Essex and the east left London through Commercial Road and East India Dock Road, and over the River Lea, which was bridged in 1810. It ran through Newhams Way, Alfreds Way and Ripple Road (now the A123) in Barking, and the modern A13 bypasses much of the East End when it meets the Thames Gateway at Dagenham, opened in 1999, where the older route took the line of the A1306.

Southend did not enjoy the boom that new roads brought to towns such as Margate, Ramsgate and Brighton in the Georgian period, since the roads leading to it were not sufficiently good to popularise it as a leisure destination. But in the nineteenth century, Southend's popularity as a seaside resort began to grow, and its famous pleasure pier – still the longest in the world – was constructed. The Southend arterial road, the A127, which was opened in the 1920s, is the only other main route out of Southend.

MAP 25

1. Which artist, born in Barking, included the song 'A13: Trunk Road to the Sea' on his *Peel Sessions* album released in 1991?

2. Which place is an anagram of BORED TOWN?

3. Which place on the Thames estuary was devastated in 1953 by a North Sea flood?

4. Essex stronghold overlooking the Thames.

5. Stony ford on optimistic river.

6. What connects Hull, Battles, and Hey?

7. Foreign abode.

8. Distance from Chelmsford to Rayleigh.

9. Hamlet, whose name connects 'out', 'about' and 'up'.

10. Brush? Something to do with clothes.

Opposite: Extract from *The AA Complete Road Atlas of Britain, 5th edition* (1983), at a scale of 1:250,000.

Mapping milestone

In 1925 we published the classic touring guide, *The AA Road Book of England and Wales*. Together, our accurate mapping and in-depth knowledge of places to visit became a benchmark for British travel publishing.

THE ATLANTIC HIGHWAY
A39

The idea of an Atlantic Highway was conceived as a pure marketing exercise by the Bude Tourist Board in 1988. They came up with the idea of naming the A39 the Atlantic Highway, inspired by Southern Railway's Atlantic Coast Express, which ran from 1926 until 1966.

The A39 itself is just over two hundred miles long and stretches from Falmouth in Cornwall to Bath in Somerset. The road mainly follows the old turnpike roads.

The seventy-mile section branded the Atlantic Highway runs from Fraddon in Cornwall through to the junction with the A361 at Barnstaple in North Devon. Within Cornwall, the road links the north coast towns of Bude and Newquay.

Throughout the 1990s the route name was marketed in Tourist Board leaflets, and in 2002 the route was officially brown-signposted 'Atlantic Highway'. But in the same year the road lost its trunk road status, and more recently has been cited as the most dangerous road in the southwest.

MAP 26

1.   What alternative, slightly faster route would take you from Fraddon to Barnstaple?

2.   How many saints are there west of the River Tamar?

3.   You can find the Tate here.

4.   'By Tre, Pol and Pen you will know the Cornishmen'. Given that 'Tre' means town, 'Pol' means pool and 'Pen' is found near the start of the A39, what might 'Pen' mean?

5.   Britain's most south-westerly airport.

6.   Which place is an anagram of OBSTACLES?

7.   What connects Newton and Milton?

8.   Birthplace of legendary king.

9.   Location used for the TV series *Doc Martin*.

10. If the second part was removed you might have to do the first part!

Opposite: This map is taken from *The AA Glovebox Britain, 16th edition* (2018). Although the original map is 1:500,000 scale, it has been scaled down here to fit.

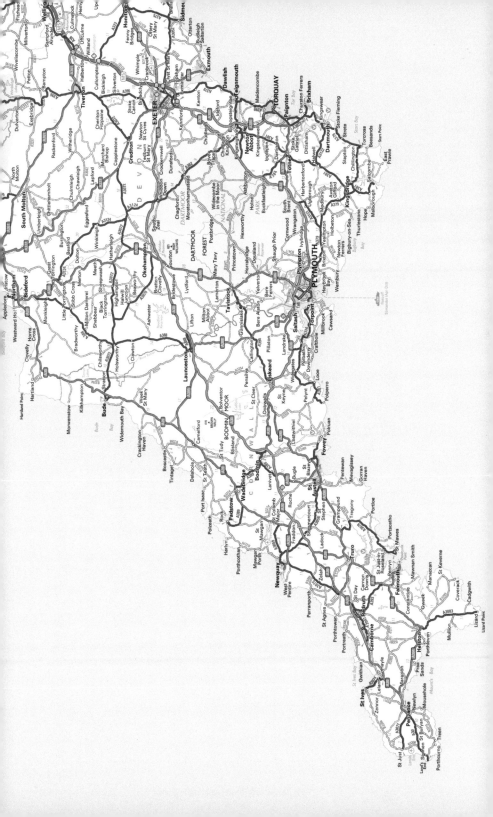

About the map

We've chosen the most scenic section of the SWC300 for this puzzle: the route between Dumfries in the east and Cairnryan in the west. The mapping comes from *The AA Glovebox Britain, 16th edition* (2018) and is at 1:500,000 scale. Working your way around the coast, you leave Dumfries on the A710, then take the A711, the B727, the A75, the A714 and the B roads closest to the coast, before joining the A747, B7084 and A716 down to the Mull of Galloway. Taking the A77, you follow the road up the west coast.

THE SOUTH WEST
COASTAL 300

Look at this area of Britain on a map and you notice something peculiar: the country is divided into nine zones along the lines of its motorways, and yet there is no M7. Telford's nineteenth-century coaching route between Carlisle and Glasgow, which became the A74, has stood the test of time as a perfectly good route, and was simply upgraded to become the A74(M). The area sitting to the west of the A74(M), where all roads take a '7' prefix, covers the Galloway Forest Park and South Ayrshire countryside.

The South West Coastal 300 is a recently invented touring route, one of a number of Scottish touring routes designed to promote local businesses and attract tourists into the country. The SWC300 takes you along 304 miles of quiet roads through Dumfries and the south-west coast of Scotland.

There is no official starting place on this loop, but you can trace the line along the A74, into Lockerbie, across to Dumfries, and then it drops down to follow the coastal route west all the way across to the Mull of Galloway and then up the coast to Turnberry Bay and Ayr before heading inland again to pass New Cumnock and the line of the A74(M). The touring route avoids the motorway altogether by opting for the slower-paced B7076, which runs parallel.

MAP 27

1. Which place is an anagram of GENIAL SORT?

2. Additional practice of percussion needed.

3. What connects Patrick, William and Logan?

4. What is the distance from New Galloway to Pinwherry via Newton Stewart?

5. Starting place of the River Dee.

6. Stagecoaches from Dumfries to Stranraer would have stopped to pay a toll here.

7. Name of the strait separating Cumbria from Dumfries and Galloway.

8. Southernmost point of Scotland.

9. Natural harbour for ferries to Northern Ireland.

10. The French Disney.

Opposite: See p.138 for details of the map.

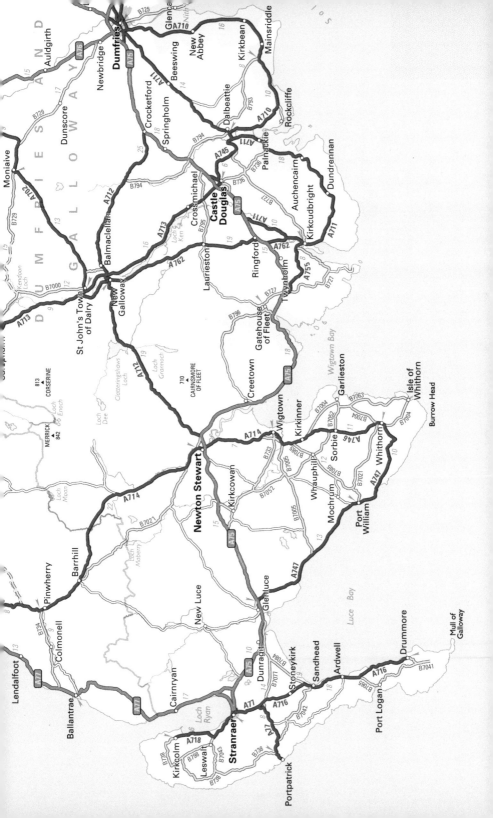

I'm now arrived – thanks to the gods! –
Thro' pathways rough and muddy,

A certain sign that makin roads
Is no this people's study:

Robert Burns 'Epigram on Rough Roads' (1786)

THE ROAD TO APPLECROSS
A896

Bealach na Bà, often shortened to 'The Bealach', is the only road to Applecross unless you follow the winding coastal road from Shieldaig around the peninsula. Bealach na Bà means 'Pass of the Cattle', which gives the clue to its ancient origins as a drovers' route. Built in 1822, it looks as if it belongs in the Alps: a single-track road winding around hairpin bends. The road is one of Britain's steepest, with a sign issuing a warning about the journey to come: 'This road rises to a height of 2053 ft with gradients of 1 in 5 and hairpin bends'. It is Scotland's third-highest road, almost as high as Cairnwell Pass (*see Puzzle 40*).

Inhabitants of Applecross don't use this name to refer to their village, although the name Applecross is at least 1,300 years old. To them it is simply 'the street'. Sit in the Applecross Inn, dating from the 1800s, and you have views out across Applecross Bay to the Isles of Raasay and Skye. This eleven-mile route is one of the most famous sections of the North Coast 500 route (*see p.123*). Until the 1950s, parts of the road were still gravel and impassable during bad weather. It wasn't until the 1990s that the dry-stone walls protecting drivers from the treacherous drops at the side of the road were replaced with metal crash barriers.

MAP 28

1. Which fictional police officer was featured in an eponymous TV series driving on this road with a sign 'Narrow Road – No more than Three Sheep Abreast'?

2. Sea loch with Ardarroch on its edge.

3. What connects Tuath, Breac, Arachaidh and Gaineamhach?

4. A Munro is a Scottish mountain over 3,000 ft (914.4 m); a Corbett is over 2,500 ft (762 m), and a Graham is over 2,000 ft (609.6 m). Which of these (with heights marked) can be seen on the map?

5. This area of Scotland sounds like a continent from *Game of Thrones*.

6. Island of Cattle?

7. Paradise Regained?

8. Gaelic has many names for hills. What's the difference between a Carn (or Cairn) and a Creag?

9. In Gaelic the compass directions are tuath (north), deas (south), ear (east), and iar (west). Which place on the map has one of these in its name?

10. Strand outside Los Angeles with a ban on returning.

Opposite: Extract from *The AA Close-Up Britain Atlas, 2nd edition* (2008). The scale of the original map is 1:100,000, but it has been reproduced here at a slightly larger scale to better show the detail on this road.

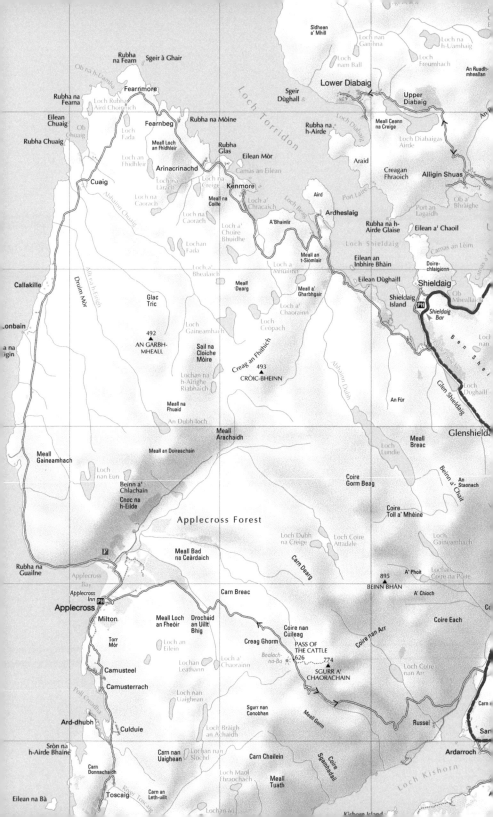

Mapping milestone

By 1926 we were publishing tours as well as routes. Tours could take several days and the information included remarks about scenery and advice about ferry crossings. We began to add 'strip maps' to our route sheets as a further navigational aid. By 1929 we were issuing 239,000 routes a year. These were improved in the 1930s with the addition of mileages.

THE DRAGON'S SPINE
A470

The A470 can't be said to have much provenance as a complete route in itself. It started as a road between Cardiff and the Breacons, but having adopted and renumbered older roads, today it forms a complete 185 mile (299 km) coast-to-coast route across Wales, from Llandudno in the north to Cardiff in the south.

Starting at Llandudno on the north coast, the road winds south along the Conwy valley. It crosses Telford's A5 at Betws-y-coed (*see Puzzle 10*), and runs through the Lledr valley and Gwydr Forest Park, before making the steep ascent through the mountains of Snowdonia. Descending to Blaenau Ffestiniog, home of the Ffestiniog Railway, it then climbs back up through Ffestiniog. After crossing wild moorland, it descends into the Eden valley through the Coed-y-Brenin Forest and reaches Dolgellau.

Next, the A470 climbs through the Cambrian Mountains – the Green Desert of Wales – before descending into the Dyfi valley, and taking a south-east turn to follow the railway line towards Talerddig. After following the Afon Carno down to Caersws and the River Severn, the road turns right and follows the Severn valley to Llanidloes and Llangurig, before pointing south-west again.

Winding its way through the wooded Wye Valley, it then climbs up to the city of Brecon, and takes a dramatic scenic route across the Brecon Beacons and into Merthyr Tydfil. The final stretch is dual carriageway through the South Wales Coalfield and into Cardiff.

MAP 29

1. Which town on this route is the exact mid-point of Wales and sits on the River Severn?

2. Which place is an anagram of PANTHER?

3. A famous BBC sci-fi show is recorded and produced here.

4. Tramways, canals and railways all transported coal from the South Welsh Coalfields to the nearest ports. Name two major docks shown on the map used to ship this coal.

5. What alternative, faster route could you take between Cardiff and Llandudno?

6. The A470 travels through which two forest parks in Snowdonia?

7. Which of these Welsh rivers does the A470 not cross: Wye, Dovey, Conwy, Dee, Severn?

8. What connects Bar, Mon, and Avon?

9. To become an end-to-end trunk road, the A470 borrowed sections from various other A roads. Which road was requisitioned at Dolgellau?

10. Constructed High School outside satisfactorily.

Opposite: This very small-scale map (1:1 million), extracted from The AA's 2019 Great Britain mapping database, shows the entire length of the coast-to-coast trunk road.

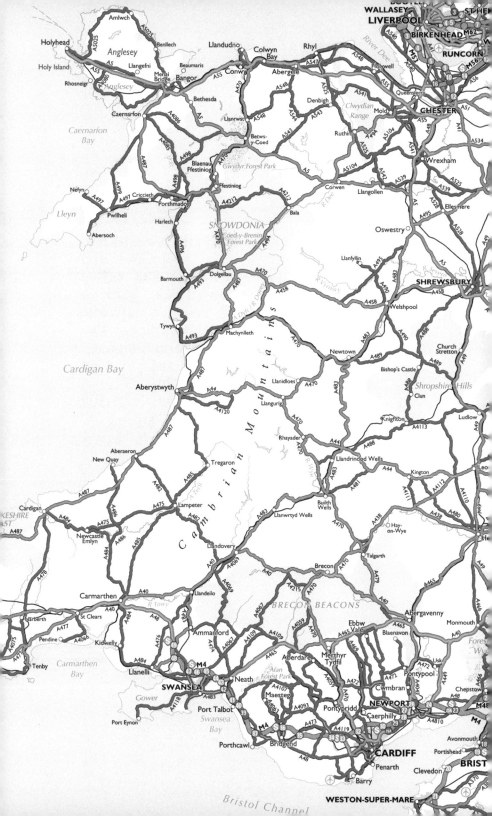

618. YORK to WHITBY. As 617 to Malton; wild, unfenced moorland and fine views, later crossing the Esk valley with maximum gradient 1—5. Whitby picturesque but with narrow streets. An exposed route in bad weather. The side run to Goathland is recommended.

		York* ..	..	46½	A.64
10¼	10¼	Barton Hill	..	36¼	..
17½	7¼	**Malton***	..	29	A.169
18¾	1¼	Old Malton	..	27¾	..
26	7¼	Pickering*	..	20½	..
34	8	Saltersgate Hotel*	..	12½	..
42¼	8¼	Sleights	..	4¼	..
44½	2¼	Ruswarp	..	2	..
46½	2	**Whitby***	..		..

The AA Road Book of England and Wales (1938)

THE NORTH YORK MOORS
A169

This classic route is illustrated with a map from *The AA Road Book of England and Wales* (1938). Looking at the road numbering you might be justifiably confused. The Ministry of Transport Act 1919 had established a Ministry of Transport and with it the right for the minister to create a road classification system. A list of Class I and Class II roads was published in 1923, followed by annual updates and a major revision in 1935.

This map, however, shows an entirely different numbering system, based on AA touring route numbers. The route number from York to Whitby via Pickering refers to Route 618 (*see opposite*).

The A169 runs from the edge of the Yorkshire Wolds at Pickering and across the North York Moors. An impressive dip in the landscape 394 ft (120 m) deep and ¾ mile (1.2 km) wide can be seen to the west, known as the Hole of Horcum. Legend has it this was made by a giant called Wade, who picked up a clump of earth (now known as Blakey Topping) and threw it at his wife.

At the bottom of a zig-zag section of the road known as the Devil's Elbow is the site of the recently-demolished Saltersgate Inn. For years the pub was used by smugglers bringing salt across the moors from Whitby and Robin Hood's Bay, avoiding the salt tax.

Running close by is George Stephenson's North York Moors Railway, built to improve trade routes with the port of Whitby.

MAP 30

1. Which TV series, set in the 1950s in the fictional village of Aidensfield in the North Riding of Yorkshire, was filmed at Goathland along this route?

2. Once home to Cistercian nuns.

3. Name two other routes that share part of the York to Whitby route. Where do they begin and end?

4. What distance is the route from York to Whitby?

5. Which place is an anagram of A NORTHERN TOLL?

6. Which market town due south of Scarborough has one of Britain's largest parish churches?

7. Put these in order from north to south: Yorkshire Wolds Way, Esk Dale, Newton Dale.

8. Which famous 'way' runs from Helmsley to Scarborough?

9. Sum of the routes out of York.

10. Rowing crews on middle of isle (*Hint*: see route detail on p.150).

Opposite: Extract from *The AA Road Book of England and Wales* (1938), at a scale of 12 miles to the inch.

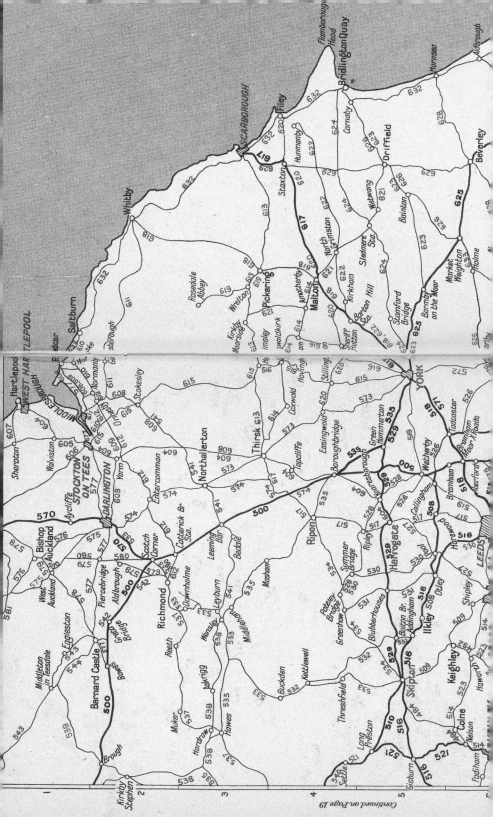

Continued on Page 19

ROUNDABOUTS
AND ROAD SYSTEMS

The first circular interchanges where several roads joined were known as circuses, circus being Latin for 'circle'. London's Piccadilly Circus, Oxford Circus and Cambridge Circus were all effectively early roundabouts.

But the first modern roundabout system was designed by William Phelps Eno for Columbus Circle in New York and opened in 1905. Britain's first modern roundabout emerged just a few years later, described as a 'gyratory flow' system. It was designed for Letchworth Garden City in 1909 at Sollershot Circus, and its centre was originally intended for use as a traffic island for pedestrians. In and around Birmingham, roundabouts are still sometimes confusingly referred to as islands.

Following the construction of the new traffic circle at Hyde Park Corner in 1926, the new term 'round-about' was coined in *The Times* 'to express the new traffic arrangements' in opposition to the 'uncouth' word 'gyratory'. Since then, gyratory has tended to be used for very large circular intersections, often with buildings occupying the central island, and where the rules or road markings may not be standard.

Roundabouts were re-engineered and standardised in the UK in 1966, when for the first time a clear set of rules could be applied to these circular junctions. Frank Blackmore of the Transport Research Laboratory created the 'priority rule' to give way to traffic on your right, which increased safety and made these circular, clockwise, one-way traffic systems much easier to use.

Opposite: Aerial view of Gravelly Hill Interchange (Spaghetti Junction), 2008 / Highways Agency.

Multiple roundabouts

At some complex junctions, there may be a series of mini-roundabouts at each intersection. Treat each mini-roundabout separately and follow the normal rules.

The Highway Code

THE MAGIC ROUNDABOUT

A magic roundabout is officially known as a 'ring junction', and the first and still best-known is Swindon's. Designed by Frank Blackmore, inventor of the mini-roundabout and the priority rule, it was constructed in 1972 and named after the children's television series *The Magic Roundabout*.

What was magic about it? The traffic could flow clockwise and anticlockwise. The main island is surrounded by five mini roundabouts, offering multiple paths between its entries and exits. An anticlockwise flow of traffic is created in the inner lane as traffic circles round the mini roundabouts.

The roundabout is built near to Swindon's football club, over a section of the old Swindon canal. During its pilot phase, a police officer stood at each mini roundabout helping to direct the traffic.

Despite being widely considered a particularly hairy intersection, the roundabout has proven to be remarkably safe, presumably because its complexity leads to some people avoiding it altogether and others navigating it very slowly and carefully.

Other examples of magic roundabouts include the Plough Roundabout in Hemel Hempstead with its six mini roundabouts; the roundabout carrying the A40 and A404 in High Wycombe; the Denham Roundabout near Uxbridge; and the Greenstead Roundabout in Colchester.

MAP 31

1.   What do the blue letters SN1 denote?

2.   What connects J2 with H5?

3.   Name of the dog and talking jack-in-the-box from *The Magic Roundabout*?

4.   Named after the father of geometry.

5.   Given the map's scale of 1:10,000 (or 6.3 inches to 1 mile), how far is Old Town roundabout from the Magic Roundabout as the crow flies?

6.   Named after British Liberal prime minister.

7.   Driving from Upham Road to Queen's Drive, what's the minimum number of right turns you could make?

8.   Which 1982 song from XTC was inspired by Swindon's Magic Roundabout?

9.   If you were to approach the Magic Roundabout from Drove Road and drive clockwise around each small island, anticlockwise around the central island and back into Drove Road, what distance would you have travelled in total? Assume the diameter of each mini roundabout is 46 m and the central roundabout is 126 m.

10. Do a summer's work – or day shifts.

Opposite: Extract from *AA Street by Street Swindon* (2001), at a scale of 1:10,000.

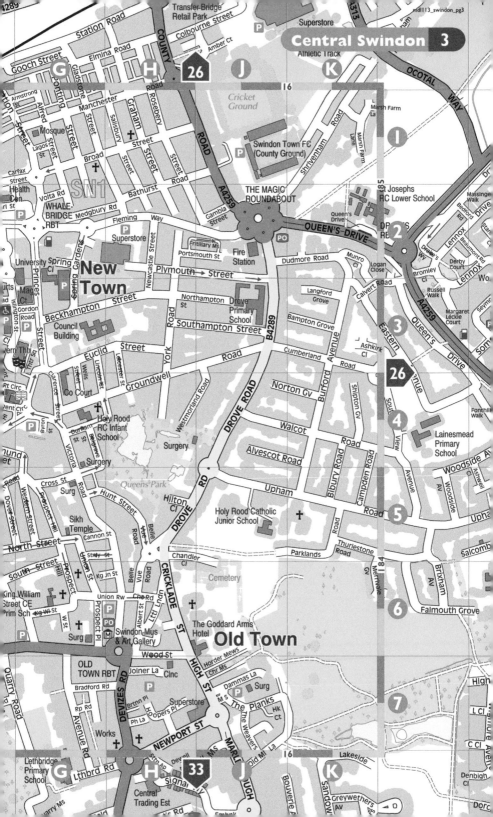

4289

Transfer Bridge
Retail Park
Colbourne Street

Superstore

Station Road

Gooch Street

Elmina Road

G **H** **26** **J** **K**

OCOTAL WAY

Amber Ct

Athletic Track

4313

Cricket Ground

16

Marsh Farm La

I

Armstrong St

Ponting Street

Gladstone Street

Manchester Street

Salisbury Street

Rosebery Street

Road

Alfred St

Mosque

Lagos St

Broad

Volta Rd

Carfax street

Health Cen

SN1

WHALE-BRIDGE RBT

Medgbury Rd

Bathurst Street

Graham Street

Fleming Way

Swindon Town FC (County Ground)

Shrivenham Road

Marsh Farm Lane

St Josephs RC Lower School

Massinge Walk

Bedford Rd

Lennox Rd

Beaumont Rd

Stan

THE MAGIC ROUNDABOUT

Queen's Drive

2

Drakes Way

Bromley Cl

Derby Court

Lennox

Wo

University Cl

Spring Cl

Princes

Mags Ct

Gordon Road

Gardens

Superstore

Newcastle Street

Frittilary Ms

Portsmouth St

Fire Station

PO

Dudmore Road

Munro Cl

Logan Close

Calvert Road

Queen's Drive

Eastern

A4259

Margaret Leckie Court

Seymr

Som

New Town

Plymouth Street

Northampton St

Drove Primary School

Langford Grove

Bampton Grove

3

Ashkirk Cl

Beckhampton Street

Council Building

York Road

Southampton Street

B4289

Cumberland Road

Burford Avenue

Shipton Gv

South View

26

Fonthill Walk

Euclid Street

Wells Street

Lincoln St

Leicester St

Groundwell Road

Norton Gv

Bibury Road

Campden Road

Road

Avenue

Av

Woodside Av

Woodside Av

4

Lainesmead Primary School

Astwell

Upha

Holy Rood RC Infant School

Durham St

Belgrave

Surgery

Westmorland Road

DROVE ROAD

Walcot

Alvescot Road

Road

5

Victoria Road

Surgery

Cross St

Surg

Hunt Street

Queen's Park

Hilton Cl

DROVE RD

Belle

Upham

Road

Thurlestone Road

Gv

Merivale

Salcomb

Western Street

Prospect Hill

Sikh Temple

North Street

Cannon St

Chandler Cl

Holy Rood Catholic Junior School

Parklands

Brixham Av

Falmouth Grove

6

Dover Street

South Street

Prospect

Union St

Stuly st

Belle Vue Road

Cemetery

King William Street CE Prim Sch

Kg Wl St

Union Rw

Albert St

Che Rd

P

PO

M

Swindon Mus & Art Gallery

CRICKLADE ST

Chr Ms

Dammas La

Surg

The Goddard Arms Hotel

Old Town

Horder Mews

High

7

L Cl

Surg

OLD TOWN RBT

Bradford Rd

Joiner La

Clnc

HIGH ST

MS

P

M S

Superstore

The Planks

Hk Ct

The Weavers

C Cl

Quarry Road

Avenue Rd

DEVIZES RD

Rp Rd

Brtnn Pl

Ph La

Hoopers Pl

Works

NEWPORT ST

MARLBO ROUGH

Old Ml La

Lethbridge Primary School

Lthbrd Rd

G **H** **33** **J** **K**

Devell

Signal

Central Trading Est

Embank

16

Lakeside

Bouverie Av

Sandown Av

Greywethers Av

Denbigh Cl

Dorc

Co-operating and queuing accordingly with our fellow drivers, we wait for a gap and join the gentle gyratory flow in our own time, signalling our intentions and leaving at our chosen exit. Never is a road system better suited to the English consciousness than one that involves a set of rules and guidelines that harbours a carefully balanced system that relies on etiquette and protocol.

The UK Roundabout Appreciation Society

ROUNDABOUT CITY

In 1967 the go-ahead was given for the new town of Milton Keynes to be built. Learning from the garden city movement at the start of the century, and the other new towns that had been built following World War II, it was designed on a huge grid system with a central park and shopping centre. It was the biggest planned new town that Britain had seen.

The road layout followed a street hierarchy principle, using 1 km (0.62 mile) grid squares known as 'districts'. This regular distance between roads meant that services were evenly dispersed. People would never be more than six minutes' walk from the nearest bus stop.

There were ten horizontal (H) roads and eleven vertical (V) roads, which combined to create one hundred distinct districts. Most grid squares have a central hub and their own community facilities. The design took into account the existing villages and natural lay of the land, and made the grid system sufficiently flexible that the original villages occupied the heart of their own grid-squares. Milton Keynes was already well positioned with the Watling Street (V4) route (*see Puzzle 2*) running through it and with the M1 along its east edge.

The original plans assumed a series of crossroad junctions, but these quickly evolved into roundabout junctions, which were more efficient at dealing with the traffic. Hence the town soon became known as Roundabout City. The original grid roads are carefully planned to minimise road noise and the town also has 170 miles of 'redways', a separate network of cycle and pedestrian routes.

MAP 32

1.   Which vertical is named Grafton Gate?

2.   Which place is an anagram of FAMED SHIRE?

3.   Falcon Avenue, Ravensbourne Place, Harrier Drive . . . Can you find one more place named after a bird?

4.   Two alternative names for H5.

5.   What is the connection between Padstow Avenue, Polruan Place, Bossiney Place and Pentewan Gate?

6.   Within the central 'square' of Milton Keynes, which roads would be north first street and lower eleventh street?

7.   Named after a British explorer.

8.   How many schools are shown on the map?

9.   Which two places are named after the summer solstice?

10.   A large number, taken in by dinner bell, dined.

Opposite: Extract from *AA Street by Street Milton Keynes* (2001), originally printed at a scale of 1:10,000 but reduced in size here to fit the page.

Mapping milestone

By 1965 AA membership had exceeded
3.5 million and annual demand for routes
was over 1.25 million.

SPAGHETTI JUNCTION

In the same year that Swindon would unveil its magic roundabout, further north, in the Gravelly Hill area of Birmingham, Britain's most complex interchange was opened in May 1972. Maps and atlases still use its official name, the Gravelly Hill Interchange, but it is much better known as Spaghetti Junction, the name given by journalists at the *Birmingham Evening Mail* when they reviewed the proposed plans in 1965.

It was the central feature of the Midland Links project, which aimed to join up the M1, M5 and M6 motorways, creating a non-stop link between the north-west and south-east. A total of eighteen routes are covered by the thirty-acre interchange, which includes junction 6 of the M6, the A38(M) Aston Expressway, the A38 Tyburn Road, the A5127 Lichfield Road and various unclassified roads. The grade-separated interchange joins the routes across five different levels, making it Britain's biggest interchange. Nearly 22 miles of motorway had to be raised on 559 concrete columns to maintain the routes of three canals, two railway lines and two rivers.

It was designed and engineered by Owen Williams, and took nearly four years to build at a cost of almost £10m. Its opening was delayed due to checks required on the box girders, and approximately £7m a year is spent on repair and renewal work to keep its concrete pillars and bridge supports intact. Today it is used by over 200,000 vehicles a day – at least four times the volume when it was opened.

MAP 33

1.   Name any one of the three canals that meet under this
        motorway junction.

2.   The railway line going north-east through Gravelly Hill Station
        would take you to which city?

3.   Which river runs parallel to Tame Road and under Spaghetti
        Junction?

4.   What is the sum total of all the B roads labelled on the map,
        minus the A roads shown?

5.   Sounds like the first sign of spring.

6.   Which place is an anagram of LARGE LEVY?

7.   Spaghetti Junction comprises 4 km of slip roads and 1 km of
        the M6. If a piece of spaghetti is 26 cm long, how many strands
        of spaghetti would you need to lie end to end to cover this
        route?

8.   The construction of Spaghetti Junction required 13,000 tonnes
        of steel reinforcement. How many bowls of cooked spaghetti
        does this equate to, if a single bowl weighs 150 g?

9.   The origin of which place name on the map means 'belonging
        to the Ecchles'?

10.   A good person, I talk with determination.

Opposite: Extract from *AA Street by Street West Midlands* (2007), which depicts the
interchange at a scale of 1:17,500.

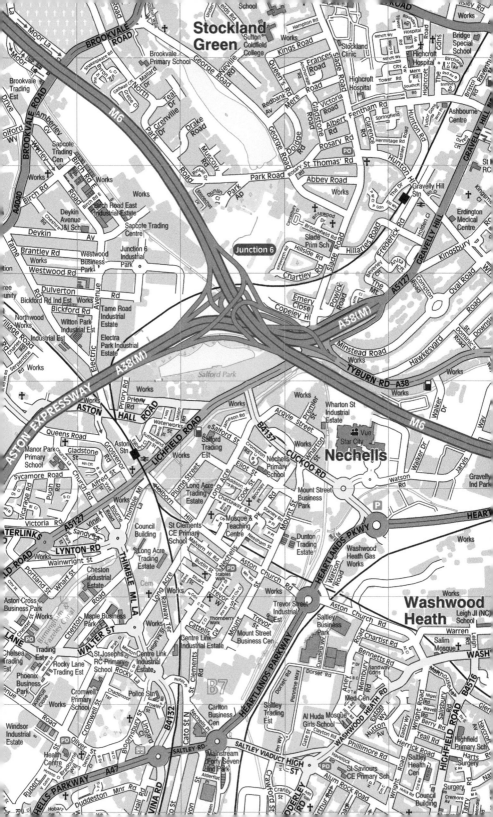

Hanger Lane /ˈhaŋə leɪn/

noun

Hanger Lane takes its name from the local area Hanger Hill, having its origin in the Old English word for a wooded slope, a hangar. Hanger Hill Park is one of the highest points in Ealing.

HANGER LANE GYRATORY

Hanger Lane Circus, later the Hanger Lane Gyratory, is a huge roundabout occupying 30,000 square metres on the North Circular (*see Puzzle 20*). It forms an interchange between the North Circular (A406), Western Avenue (A40) and Hanger Lane (A4005) in Ealing. The Hanger Lane underground station, which was opened in 1947, sits underneath the junction.

Roundabout islands have often been adopted by local councils, used for local business advertising, sculptures, flower planting and fountains. The Hanger Lane Gyratory houses a nature reserve on its central island recognised as a Site of Importance for Nature Conservation.

At its widest point, the gyratory holds eight lanes and 10,000 cars during its busiest periods. Nicknamed 'malfunction junction', it has been voted one of Britain's most terrifying junctions.

MAP 34

1. Given this map is at a scale of 3.2 inches to 1 mile, roughly how far is West Acton station from Hanger Lane station, as the crow flies?

2. Which royal road name appears twice on the map, belonging to two totally different roads?

3. The River Brent acts as the boundary between which two London boroughs?

4. Northfields, Westfields, Eastfields, Lowfield, and Highfield roads are all close to which sports club?

5. What is the stretch of A40 between Western Avenue and Paddington better known as?

6. What connects croft, crest, park and side?

7. Pitshanger Park, just north of Pitshanger Lane, has what sporting facility?

8. Western Avenue features in which 1973 novel by J. G. Ballard about symphorophilia?

9. Which underground line is Hanger Lane on?

10. Stop and leave two small boys.

Opposite: Extract from *AA Street by Street Greater London* (2002), showing the junction at a scale of 1:20,000.

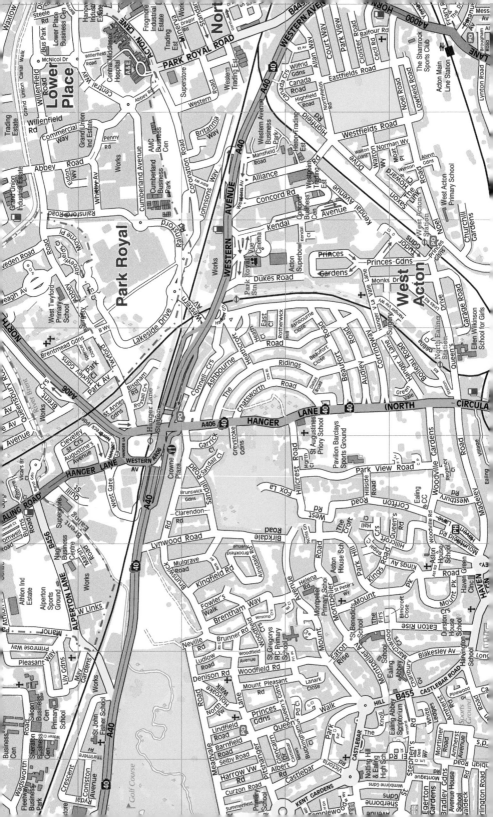

RECORD-BREAKING ROADS

Since 1910, The AA's maps and atlases have become as trusted as its patrols. The AA's cartography department grew from the very first handwritten routes, supplied to members to help them get easily and reliably to their destination. Over the years it has provided members with answers to some interesting questions, which have inspired this section of the book. Here are a few examples:

What is the lowest bridge height?
The Forth & Clyde Canal aqueduct bridges over Auchendavie Road in Kirkintilloch, giving a vehicle clearance height of just 4 ft 9 in (1.3 m).

What is the highest motorway?
Cutting across the Pennines, the M62 reaches its summit at junction 22 on Moss Moor more than 1,148 ft (350 m) above sea level.

What is the longest road tunnel?
Opened in 1934, the Mersey Tunnel is 2.87 miles (4.62 km) in length including approaches and branch tunnels.

What is the lowest A road?
The A1101 between Bury St Edmunds and Long Sutton is barely above sea level for much of its length.

What is Britain's most central location?
The geographic centre of Britain is Dunsop Bridge, off the B6478, just north of Clitheroe.

Many other record-breaking statistics have already been included throughout this book, but the puzzles that follow are based on a selection of our favourite record-breaking roads in Britain.

Opposite: Photochrom Print Collection / Ambleside, Kirkstone Pass, Lake District, between 1890 and 1900

REPRINTED FROM

THE  TIMES

Thursday November 25 1937

A HIGHWAYS PLAN

COORDINATION OF DEVELOPMENT

A.A. AND A NATIONAL PROGRAMME

A provisional scheme for the development of the main highways of Great Britain in order of their importance as traffic arteries, which has been prepared by the Automobile Association, was outlined yesterday by the secretary, Sir responsible to the Minister of Transport, with duties and functions analogous to those carried out by Telford a century ago.

All the roads are numbered on the accompanying map. The first six, in order, are:—

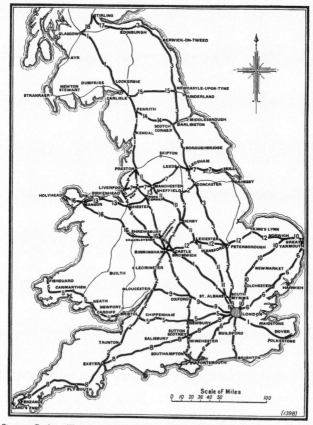

Stenson Cooke. The plan provides for the coordinated treatment of 18 highways of major importance—in two instances roads are coupled—and it is proposed that each of these should be in the charge of a road engineer, appointed by and directly

Dover—Glasgow
Exeter—Doncaster
Brighton—Edinburgh
{ Southampton—Birmingham
{ Liverpool—Preston
London—Bristol (across the Severn)—Fishguard
Portsmouth—London—Yarmouth

FIRST MOTORWAY

In 1946 the Ministry of War Transport published a blueprint for motorways, known as 'special roads'. Three years later, The Special Roads Act of 1949 authorised the construction of what became known as the motorways. These arterial routes would split England and Wales into six zones along the lines of its M1–M6 routes, and Scotland into three zones with the M7, M8 and M9. Pedestrians, cyclists and vehicles below a certain engine size would be prohibited from using the roads.

Planning for the Preston bypass had started in 1937, as part of an early plan for the M6, despite there being no legislation to build such a road at that time. The first 8.25-mile (13.3 km) stretch of motorway was opened on 5 December 1958, only five months late despite delays due to the British rain. It cost nearly £3m to build and ran from Bamber Bridge (now junction 29 of the M6) to Broughton (now junction 1 of the M55).

Then, as today, congestion in this area was a problem. Had it not been for the endless tailbacks caused by traffic flooding the A6 road to see the Blackpool illuminations, engineer James Drake may never have been commissioned to design the road. Although he felt three lanes in each direction would be necessary, he was restricted to two, so built a large central reservation zone, which could accommodate a third lane at a later date (finally added in 1966). In the 1990s it was upgraded to four lanes in each direction. The term 'hard shoulder' was coined because the shoulders were gravelled rather than tarmacked.

MAP 35

1. Which British prime minister opened the road and was the first person in Britain to travel on a motorway?

2. No speed limit was enforced for the first few years – the average speed recorded was 50 mph. True or false?

3. The road had to bridge two rivers: can you name one of them?

4. Which is Britain's longest motorway, the M6 or the M1?

5. What does the grey line, which finishes in the sea north of Southport, denote?

6. Which town on the map is known locally as Skem?

7. Home to some of the biggest brands in motor manufacturing.

8. What was used for the first time in building the Preston bypass, to replace the red-lantern paraffin burners previously used?

9. Given a scale of 4 miles to the inch, what is the approximate distance from Preston to Blackpool by motorway?

10. Izaak was first with the beer.

Opposite: This map of the Preston bypass is taken from *The AA Complete Road Atlas Britain, 9th edition* (1986), shown at a scale of 1:250,000.

Mapping milestone

In 1999 the first AA route was calculated online, and for the first time our routes were available free to members and non-members alike. This development changed the way customers accessed travel information. Between 2000 and 2010 The AA Route Planner helped motorists travel approximately 125 billion miles. This astounding distance is the equivalent of driving around the world over 5.5 million times, or 700 round trips to the sun.

STRANGEST BYPASS

This diminutive stretch of motorway south of Maidenhead was the shortest motorway in Britain when it was built, at just 828 m (2,717 ft). It sits at the very oddly numbered junction 8/9 of the M4, and to explain that numbering is to tell the story of its origin.

The section of the M4 shown on the map was originally built in 1961 as the Maidenhead bypass, which ran from junction 7 in the east to junction 9 in the west (what is now junction 9b of the A404(M)).

When the decision was made to extend the M4 west to bypass Reading, the proposed route went south, rather than north as originally planned. So the M4 continued not from where the Maidenhead bypass had ended at junction 9, but from a point in the middle, very close to junction 8.

The original junction 8 was therefore closed and a new grade-separated junction was opened, labelled 8/9. The tail end of what used to be the M4 Maidenhead bypass was renamed as the A404(M) – itself an impressively short stretch of motorway. Then a new motorway spur – the A308(M) – was built to maintain the connection between the M4 and A308, which had been lost with the closure of junction 8.

MAP 36

1. What connects wick, road and field?

2. Made arch-fiend upset.

3. Road named after Royal house.

4. Maidenhead Bridge over the Thames was built in 1777 and became the route for which 'Great' road?

5. Brunel's Great Western Railway cuts through two waterway channels to the west of The Thames: York Stream and Moor Cut. Using the surrounding road names as a clue, which is the easterly and which is the westerly channel?

6. A park that shares its name with the tragic 2017 London fire.

7. Given a scale of 3.6 inches to one mile, estimate the distance as the crow flies between Maidenhead's rowing club and its golf club.

8. The A330 would take you towards the home of which famous racecourse?

9. Travelling north, the A308 takes you from Maidenhead to which town?

10. Conduit always in need of replacing.

Opposite: Extract from *AA Street by Street Slough, Windsor, Maidenhead 2nd edition* (2006), showing the bypass at a scale of 1:17,500.

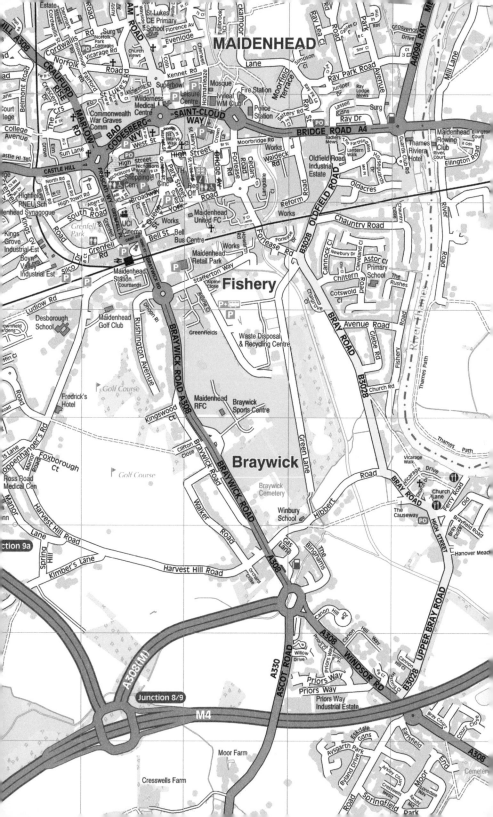

Mapping milestone

The early Roman 'road map', known as the Antonine Itinerary, registered the stations and distances along roads of the Roman Empire. The British section of the itinerary is known as the *Iter Britanniarum*, and showed distances in Roman miles, where one thousand paces equalled one Roman mile, approximately equal to 0.9 mile today. Rest houses would have existed at every fifteen miles, approximately a day's walk.

LONGEST STRAIGHT ROAD
A15

The record for Britain's longest straight road goes to an eighteen-mile section of the A15. It starts a few miles north of Lincoln, where Ermine Street (*see Puzzle 1*) met the end of the Fosse Way (*see Puzzle 3*).

This straight stretch of the A15 starts near Hackthorn (just after RAF Scampton, where the road bends) and charts the ruler-straight course of Ermine Street to Scawby (just before meeting junction 4 of the M180).

Scawby is an ancient village where archaeologists have unearthed Neolithic–Bronze Age implements and Roman and medieval pottery. Remains of a Roman villa have been found at Sturton Farm. Beyond this eighteen-mile section, the road reaches Winteringham, where the Romans would have crossed the Humber estuary to continue their journey north to York.

MAP 37

1. In what county is this record-breaking road found?

2. Eighteenth-century British landscape painter.

3. These two places are bound to cheer you up.

4. The map features which defunct roadside restaurant chain and which branches are shown on the map?

5. What does the bull symbol on the A15 indicate?

6. Holy land.

7. Which is the greater distance (as the crow flies): that which is between the two places on the map with the suffix '-xby', or between the two places with the suffix '-awby'?

8. North of Gainsborough there are three pairs of villages either side of the River Trent once linked by a river ferry. Can you name them?

9. Which abandoned village, shown on the map, was described by the Yorkshire antiquary, Abraham de la Pryme, as *'exceeding famous for robberys, and that nobody inhabited there but thieves: and that the countrey, having for a long while endur'd all their villanys, they at last, when they could suffer them no longer, riss [rose] with one consent, and pulled down the same about their ears'*?

10. Journalist, however, seen with sailors.

Opposite: Extract from *The AA Great Britain Road Atlas 2003, 17th edition* (2002), using a scale of 1:200,000.

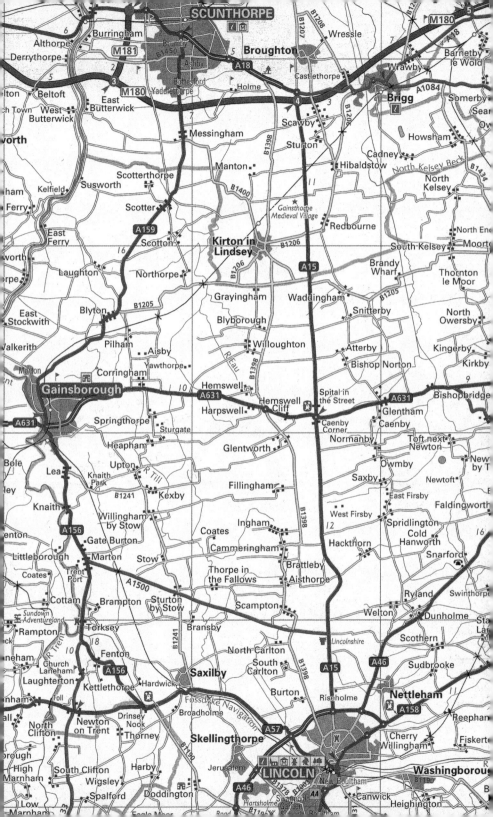

Steep hill downwards
(10% is equivalent to 1:10)

Steep hill upwards
(20% is equivalent to 1:5)

AA Know Your Road Signs (2018)

STEEPEST ROAD

The title of 'Steepest Road in Britain' is shared between two hill passes with 1 in 3 gradients: the road known as Chimney Bank between Hutton-le-Hole and Rosedale Abbey in the North York Moors, and Hardknott Pass in the Lake District.

The stretch of road between Eskdale Green and Little Langdale in the Lake District has been chosen here because it takes you through two impressive mountain passes: Hardknott Pass, with its 33% gradient, and then, crossing the River Duddon, the road climbs back up Wrynose Pass, with its 20% gradient.

The name Hardknott means 'craggy hill' and comes from the Old Norse 'harthr' (hard) and 'knutr' (hill). Originally a Roman road (the Tenth Highway), linking Ravenglass and Ambleside, the road fell into disrepair after the fifth century but continued in use as a packhorse route.

Nearby Wrynose Pass, which takes its name from Wrynose Fell, separates the Furness Fells from the Bowfell-Crinkle Crags. It reaches an altitude of 393 m (1,281 ft), and the Three Shire Stone at the summit marks the meeting of three counties.

From Ambleside heading northeast, you climb up Kirkstone Pass – locally known as 'The Struggle' – which at 485 m (1,489 ft) has the highest summit of the three passes.

MAP 38

1. Which three historic counties meet at the Three Shire Stone?

2. What is the highest mountain on the map?

3. Estimate the distance between The Old Man of Coniston and High Seat as the crow flies, given the scale of 1:200,000.

4. Grisdale, Stickle and Seathwaite are all what?

5. After Hardknott Fell, which is the next fell on the ridge, also taking its name from the Old Norse for 'hard'?

6. Where can you take a trip on a Victorian steam-powered yacht?

7. The monks of which abbey, 25 miles to the south and named after these fells, had the grazing and hunting rights around these passes?

8. If you add together the height in metres of Hardknott, Wrynose and Kirkstone passes, and then subtract The Old Man of Coniston, what is the answer?

9. Which historic coaching inn found on this map is the third-highest in Britain?

10. Wearing warm, silky garments, girl collapsed.

Opposite: Extract from *The AA Great Britain Road Atlas 2020* (2019), which uses a scale of 1:200,000.

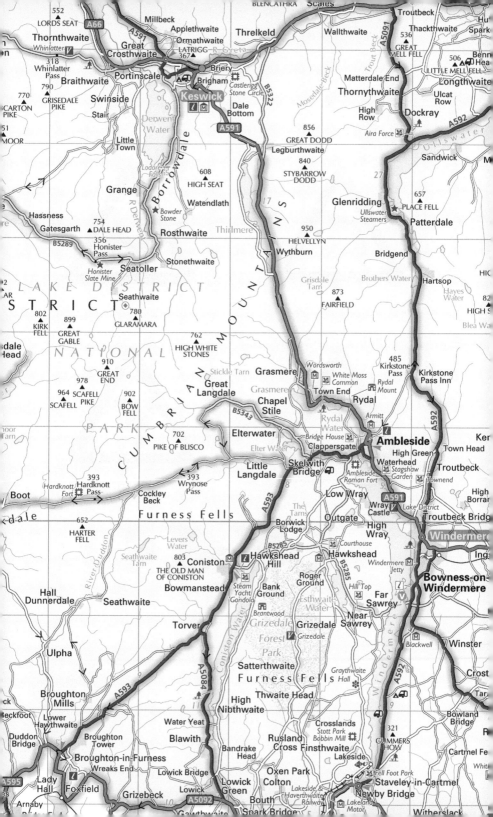

Bend to right (left if symbol is reversed)

Double bend first to the left (right if symbol is reversed)

Junction on bend

Junction on bend (reversed)

Sharp deviation of route to the left (right if chevrons reversed)

AA Know Your Road Signs (2018)

BENDIEST ROAD
B3081

This mile-long stretch of road near Shaftesbury in Dorset is said to be the bendiest road in Britain. It climbs upwards at a 10% gradient shortly after its start in the village of Cann Common, and then proceeds through narrow bends and switchbacks on its way to the Wiltshire village of Tollard Royal.

In 2006 Dorset Council was criticised for the poor surfacing of the road after a study by Continental Tyres found that by driving at 30 mph, drivers would experience the same lateral G force as they would get driving around a racetrack like Brands Hatch.

Six road warning signs with black and white chevrons indicating sharp bends can be found within a short stretch of this road as it twists to and fro.

MAP 39

1. What connects Lines, Lane and Sheet Hill?

2. Which county boundary runs through Zig-Zag Hill?

3. What is the name given to the unenclosed chalk land on this map, formerly reserved for hunting?

4. The National Trust bought Fontmell Down to conserve the landscape of which English novelist?

5. Shaftesbury town centre has views over which vale that, along with the Vale of Wardour, is part of the Stour Valley and surrounded by the Dorset Downs to the south?

6. Ridley Scott's famous 1973 advert for Hovis bread showed a boy pushing his bike up which cobbled hill in Shaftesbury?

7. What is the name of the horizonal force, provided by the friction between the tyres and the road, required for a car to travel around a bend?

8. If a car goes too quickly around a sharp bend, what is the name of the force that will pull it away from the centre and potentially into oncoming traffic?

9. Which windy summit sits about a mile and a half away to the east-northeast of Melbury Hill?

10. Indication of pause, mostly to load gun.

Opposite: Extract from *The AA Close-Up Britain Atlas, 2nd edition* (2008), which uses a scale of 1:100,000.

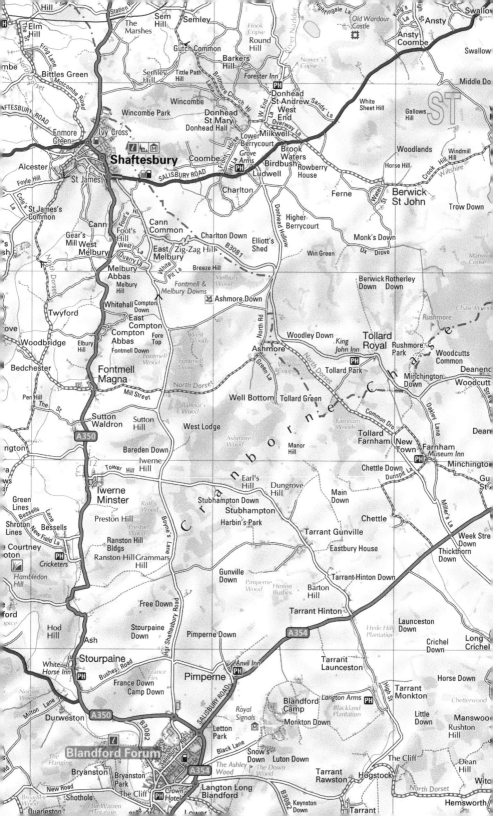

Càrn /kɑːn/ [also, Cairn]

noun

Càrn is a Gaelic word for a heap of stones or stony hill. Cairnwell is from the Gaelic 'An Càrn Bhalg', meaning the hill of bags.

HIGHEST ROAD
A93

Find Britain's largest and oldest ski resort and you'll find its highest road. Reaching an elevation of 670 m (2,199 ft), the Cairnwell Pass in the Cairngorms National Park was built in 1749 by Major William Caulfeild.

Following the plan of his predecessor, General Wade, to build a series of military roads, Caulfeild was made Inspector of Roads for Scotland in 1732. He directed the building of no less than 900 miles of new road and 600 bridges in Scotland. The A93 was part of Wade's original Perth to Fort George road.

The section of road from the Spittal of Glenshee up to Braemar, in which you find the Cairnwell Pass, was used by drovers for transporting cattle and sheep from the Lowlands to the Highlands. The boundary of Aberdeenshire and Perthshire crosses the summit of the pass.

Today the road goes more or less straight up, but earlier motorists would have had to negotiate a notorious double hairpin bend known as The Devil's Elbow, a fairly common name for a tight corner (*see Puzzle 30*). Prince Philip was famously pictured driving the Queen in her Daimler up this road to Balmoral. The old road can still be seen diverging from the new road near the start of the hill, which was built in the 1960s to bypass The Devil's Elbow.

MAP 40

1. The Spittal of Glenshee is situated where Glen Lochsie meets which other three glens?

2. What does Spittal or Spital mean?

3. Which place is an anagram of MINOR CRAGS?

4. Which Munro is situated closest to the road?

5. What might you stalk in Caenlochan Forest?

6. The Gaelic for Caenlochan is 'Cadha an Lochain', meaning 'pass of the lochan'. But what does lochan mean?

7. At its steepest the road gradient is about 17%. How many miles would you have to travel up this hill to cover the equivalent of one mile on the flat?

8. The border between which two counties crosses the summit of the pass?

9. Garrison and family home of Clan Farquharson, located to control access through the Cairngorms.

10. Bouncer is too short, just!

Opposite: Extract from *The AA Close-Up Britain Atlas, 2nd edition* (2008), scaled down here to fit the page.

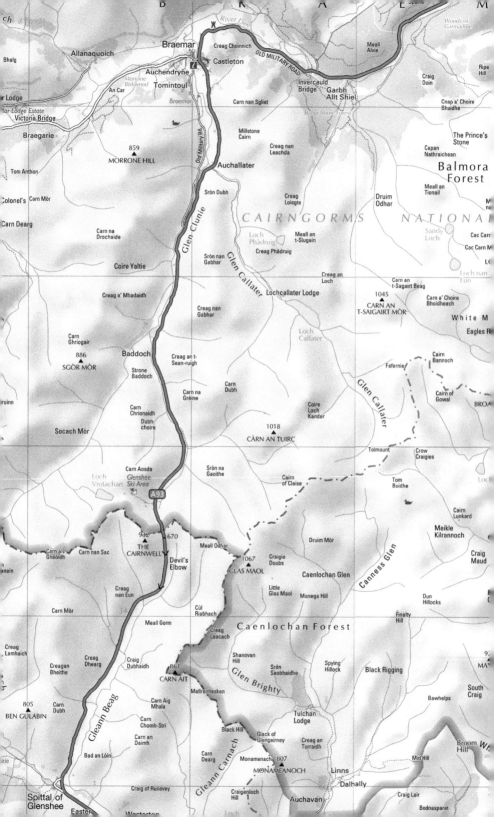

ANSWERS

Ermine Street

1. Clockwise from Bishopsgate the other original gates were Aldgate (road to Colchester); Ludgate (road to Bath); Newgate (road to Oxford) and Cripplegate (road to Islington). Aldersgate was added by the Romans two hundred years later, and finally, in 1415, Moorgate was built into the wall, becoming the last of the seven 'old gates of London'. They were destroyed between 1760–67 as part of a road-widening scheme.

2. Great Cambridge Road

3. Godmanchester

4. Caxton

5. Cambridgeshire, Bedfordshire and Huntingdonshire (which was absorbed into modern Northamptonshire in 1965).

6. The Icknield Way (A505)

7. MCCVIII (1,208 = A1 + A603 + A604). The A10 is also a Roman road, but its label lies outside the section of this map. The Icknield Way is pre-Roman.

8. 22 miles (13 + 9)

9. Old West River

10. GAMLINGAY: GAMING about L + AY

Watling Street

1. Britain's first motorway service station, Watford Gap services. Two hundred years earlier, the coaching inn at Watford Gap had provided weary travellers on the East Anglia Stagecoach route with a well-earned respite.

2. Towcester Racecourse

3. Eleanor Cross (at Hardingstone)

4. For the Grand Union Canal to pass over the River Ouse

5. 8 miles (see blue distance in miles between pointer symbols)

6. A restricted primary junction

7. Duncote

8. The A5 is roughly three miles shorter. Taking the M1 would be the quicker route by about three minutes

9. Northamptonshire County Cricket Club and Northampton Town Football Club

10. TOWCESTER: sounds like TOASTER

The Fosse Way

1. Military camp

2. Chedworth Roman Villa

3. Bourton-on-the-Water (the Cotswold Motoring Museum)

4. Batsford

5. Upper Slaughter and Lower Slaughter

6. Fossebridge and Stretton on Fosse

7. The River Stour (Shipston-on-Stour, Newbold on Stour, Preston on Stour, Atherstone on Stour) and the River Avon (Stratford Upon Avon, Weston-on-Avon, Welford-on-Avon, Bidford-on-Avon)

8. RAF Brize Norton – the RAF's largest station

9. Approximately 41 km (25.5 miles)

10. TURKDEAN: anagram of TEA DRUNK

The Hog's Back

1. Its high elevation allowed the signalling system to provide a fast communications link from London to the Royal Dockyard in Portsmouth.

2. The North Downs Way

3. Winkworth Arboretum

4. The River Wey

5. Farnham, Godalming and Woking

6. Hangman's Hill

7. The settlement was once an Anglo-Saxon village

8. 365. The primary routes are shown in green, so the sum is A3 + A31 + A331.

9. Worplesdon

10. RUNFOLD: R + UNFOLD

The Great North Road

1.   Dick Whittington

2.   Nene Valley Railway

3.   Dick Turpin

4.   Monks Wood

5.   30–35 miles

6.   Little Gidding

7.   Norman Cross (junction 16 of the A1)

8.   Sting

9.   Conington

10.   SAWTRY: they SAW a TRY

The Great Dover Road

1. Chaucer's *Canterbury Tales*

2. Hastings, New Romney, Hythe, Dover and Sandwich

3. Welling, Bexleyheath and Crayford

4. Approximately 32 miles (3.2 inches), which you can also reach by adding the black mileages shown (9 + 8 + 15 = 32).

5. Maidstone

6. Romney Marsh

7. The Swale, meaning 'swirling, rushing river' in Old English. The Isle of Sheppey is derived from the Old English 'Sceapig', meaning 'Sheep Island'.

8. Westgate-on-Sea, Margate, Kingsgate, Ramsgate, and Sandgate.

9. They all have lighthouses

10. BARHAM: BAR (save, except) + HAM

The Great Road to Land's End

1. John Betjeman

2. Approximately 50 miles

3. Brendon Hills

4. Torcross, Torquay, Torrington

5. River Exe

6. *Westward Ho!*

7. Fingle Bridge

8. Restormel Castle

9. Crediton

10. PENZANCE: PENANCE about Z

The Great West Road

1. Silbury Hill

2. The Ridgeway

3. There are seven – from north to south they are the Broad Town White Horse, Hackpen White Horse, Cherhill White Horse, Marlborough White Horse, Devizes White Horse, Alton Barnes White Horse, and Pewsey White Horse. They tell us that this is a chalk area.

4. The Cherhill White Horse (also called Oldbury White Horse)

5. Marlborough College

6. A346, A4361, B4000 and a short stretch of the A4

7. 30 miles

8. The Marlborough Downs, Bishopstone Downs, Lambourn Downs, Fyfield Down, Cherhill Down, North Down, Wilsford Down, Pewsey Down, Tidcombe Down and Heydown.

9. Caen Hill Locks

10. AVEBURY: AVE + BUY about R

Gateway to the Highlands

1. Fort William

2. The West Highland Way

3. Massacre of Glencoe

4. Steall Falls

5. Rannoch Moor

6. *Skyfall*

7. Ben Nevis

8. Meall Nan Ruadhag (Sgorr Dhonuill 1001 m + Stob Ban 999 m – Sgurr-Finnisg-Aig 662 m – Beinn Molurgainn 692 m = Meall Nan Ruadhag 646 m)

9. Glen Strae

10. TYNDRUM: sounds like TIN DRUM (Grass wrote *The Tin Drum*)

The Colossus of Roads

1. Betws-y-Coed

2. Conwy suspension bridge

3. Robert Southey

4. Bethesda

5. Four. Ffestiniog Railway; Snowdon Mountain Railway;
    Fairbourne Railway; Llanberis Lake Railway

6. Conwy; Beaumaris; Caernarfon; Dolwyddelan; Harlech. There
    is also a castle at Criccieth, not marked on this map

7. The distance is roughly 40 miles, so it would take an hour

8. (Neolithic) burial chambers

9. 1584 feet = 0.06 x 5 x 5280

10. RED WHARF BAY: RE DWARF BAY outside H

Scotch Corner

1. 6.4%.
   To answer the question, use the start value of 0.15 and the final value of 1.8, and the period of 40 years. To calculate the annual growth rate divide 1.8 by 0.15 (= 12) and take the 40th root of 12 (= 1.064) – 1 x 100 = 6.4%.

2. 11 miles

3. Head (Minehead, Headband, Gateshead)

4. Chester-le-Street

5. Birtley

6. Grade-separated roundabout

7. 18 miles

8. A689 to Hartlepool, Teeside and Bishop Auckland

9. Framwellgate Moor

10. DARLINGTON: DARLING (Grace) + TON

12

Snake Pass

1. Human League

2. National Trust

3. Glossop

4. Birds (Dove Holes, Sparrowpit, Chatsworth)

5. Great Hucklow

6. Blue John stone – a form of fluorite

7. Ladybower

8. Crowden

9. Ringinglow

10. KINDER SCOUT: reference to Scouts' motto

13

EVO Triangle

1. Gwynedd, Denbighshire and Conwy.

2. Llyn Brenig reservoir

3. Cerrigydrudion

4. 10,154 (B4501 + A5 +A543 + B5105)

5. Afon

6. 19 square miles. To calculate this, first divide the triangle, and use Pythagoras' theorem to find 'a' (i.e. $a^2 + 2.5^2 = 8^2$).

    We can then deduce that $a^2 = 57.75$ and that the $\sqrt{57.75} = 7.6$. Then we use ½ x base x height to get the solution (0.5 x 5 x 7.6 = 19).

    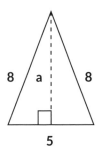

7. Valley

8. 99

9. The Archaeological Trail (along the side of Llyn Brenig)

10. GLASFRYN: anagram of SLANG about FRY

Black Mountain Road

1. It was used as flux for building materials, iron and in the production of fertiliser

2. Carreg Cennen Castle

3. Carmarthen Fan

4. Bethlehem

5. Talley Abbey

6. Mynydd Myddfai

7. Pontardawe

8. Seven Sisters

9. Carmarthenshire and Powys

10. LLANDOVERY: (A)LLY about ANDOVER

Cheddar Gorge

1. The Witch of Wookey Hole

2. Limestone

3. No it doesn't, although the labelling of 'West Country Farmhouse Cheddar' cheese is protected.

4. 8 miles (approx 5 inches)

5. 40 m. (The introduction to this road states the steepest gradient is 16%, so 0.16 x 0.25 km = 0.04 km.)

6. Easton

7. Axbridge

8. Wedmore Moor

9. Cheddar Reservoir

10. CHARTERHOUSE: i.e. house for a charter

Cat and Fiddle Road

1. The little dog

2. Long Hill (A5004)

3. 644 (= A537 + A54 +A53)

4. River Goyt

5. Whaley Bridge

6. River Dane

7. Bollington

8. The Beet

9. Lyme Park

10. SHUTLINGSLOE: sounds like 'SHUTTLING SLOW'

Honister Pass

1. Thwaite, from the Old Norse 'thveit', meaning 'clearing' or 'meadow'

2. Hay Stacks

3. 249 (Great End 910 + Great Gable 899) – (Hobcarton Pike 770 + Grisedale Pike 790)

4. Derwent Isle, Lord's Island and St Herbert's Island. Rampsholme Island, also on Derwent Water, is not marked.

5. Lodore

6. The lowest area between two peaks

7. A lake

8. The steep gradient up to Newlands Hause and back down again

9. Whinlatter Pass, which has a visitor centre

10. HONISTER: anagram of THE IRONS

The London Orbital

1. Margaret Thatcher

2. Iain Sinclair

3. *Road to Hell* by Chris Rea

4. J14 and J15 near London Heathrow Airport

5. Kent, Surrey, Buckinghamshire, Hertfordshire and Essex

6. Clacket Lane (between J5 and J6) and Cobham (between J9 and J10). Two other services, South Mimms and Thurrock, are directly accessible from it.

7. 31.5%. This is found by dividing 63,000 by 200,000 x 100.

8. 14

9. The Queen Elizabeth II bridge was opened

10. RICKMANSWORTH: RICK + MAN'S WORTH

The Golden Mile

1. High Street

2. Free flow

3. 1.7 miles (approximately 6.25 inches on the map)

4. Kew Bridge Steam Museum

5. Boston Manor Road

6. Augustus Close

7. Princess of Wales Conservatory

8. Darwin Road

9. Green Dragon Lane

10. SYON LANE: SANE about anagram of ONLY

20

The North Circular

1. Great Cambridge Interchange

2. The Brent Cross Interchange, which meets the A41 from Finchley

3. Hanger Lane gyratory system

4. The Lee Valley Viaduct over the River Lea

5. Charlie Brown's Roundabout. It was actually named after the landlord of the pub that was demolished for the roundabout's construction.

6. So that the Jewish community could cross the road on the Sabbath without using electricity or operating machinery. Traffic is held every 90 seconds between sunset on Friday and sunset on Saturday to allow pedestrians to cross.

7. Welsh Harp (near Brent Reservoir)

8. White Hart Lane

9. BARKING: BAR (the) KING

10.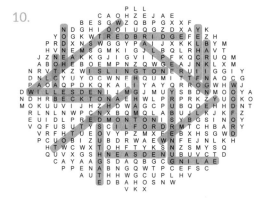

The South Circular

1. Woolwich Common, Eltham Common, Dulwich Common and Clapham Common

2. Catford

3. A junction where the routes pass at different heights (grades). Bridges and underpasses can be used so that the routes can remain continuous where they cross each other. There are two on the South Circular: one where the A2 crosses and another where the A21 crosses at the Catford gyratory system.

4. Stopping, loading or unloading

5. Windmill on the Common (PH)

6. The Valley

7. The Priory

8. Carlyle's House

9. WOOLWICH: sounds like WOOL ITCH

10.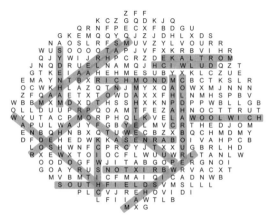

The Newbury Bypass

1. True: it was home to the Desmoulin's whorl snail, which caused the work to be delayed until the snails had been rehomed. Sadly, the species became extinct at the new site.

2. Dr David Bellamy

3. Swampy (Daniel Hooper)

4. Junction 13

5. 27 km (135mm)

6. Sandham Memorial Chapel

7. Wood

8. Highclere Castle

9. Down End, Towns End, Cottage End, East End, World's End. Pamber End is also just on the edge of the map.

10. ENBORNE ROW: WORE ROBE reversed around N and then also around N later

Highway in the Sky

1.   *Life on Mars*

2.   UMIST (now University of Manchester) and Manchester Metropolitan University

3.   Manchester Piccadilly, Oxford Road Station, Deansgate Station, Salford Central Station, Manchester Victoria Station

4.   The Metrolink or tram system

5.   Ordsall

6.   Granada Studios

7.   The River Irwell

8.   Regent Road

9.   7,399 (= A57(M) + A6042 + A665 + A635)

10. DOWNING STREET: DOWNING'S + sounds like 'TREAT'

The A303

1. 100101111

2. Hampshire, Wiltshire, Somerset and Devon

3. Take the A358 from Ilminster to join the M5 at junction 2, which takes you all the way to Exeter

4. Salisbury Plain

5. Yeovil

6. 30 miles (2.5 inches)

7. The Blackdown Hills

8. Between Ilminster and Honiton, near Marsh. Marked on the map at the boundary of grid B6/7 as 850 ft.

9. River Parrett

10. ILMINSTER: I + L + MINISTER without the second I

25

Trunk Road to the Sea

1.   Billy Bragg

2.   Brentwood

3.   Canvey Island

4.   Hadleigh Castle

5.   Stanford-le-Hope

6.   Bridge (Hullbridge, Battlesbridge and Heybridge)

7.   Dutch Cottage

8.   14 miles (as shown on the map)

9.   Mucking

10. BASILDON: BASIL (BRUSH) + DON

The Atlantic Highway

1. Driving from Fraddon, you would start out on the A30 to Oakhampton and then take the A377 and B3227 to Bideford.

2. 18. (St Just, St Ives, St Day, St Agnes, St Mawgan, St Columb Major, St Teath, St Tudy, Week St Mary, St Cleer, St Keyne, St Blazey, St Austell, St Stephen, St Mawes, St Keverne, St Just-in-Roseland, St Buryan.)

3. St Ives

4. It means headland or head (Pendennis Point and Penryn)

5. Land's End

6. Boscastle

7. Abbot

8. Tintagel

9. Port Isaac

10. WADEBRIDGE: if the BRIDGE was removed you might have to WADE!

The South West Coastal 300

1.   Garlieston

2.   Drummore

3.   Port

4.   41 miles (= 19 + 22)

5.   Loch Dee

6.   Gatehouse of Fleet

7.   Solway Firth

8.   Mull of Galloway

9.   Loch Ryan

10.   LESWALT: LES + WALT

The Road to Applecross

1. Hamish Macbeth

2. Loch Kishorn

3. Meall (hill)

4. Beinn Bhan (896 m), the highest of the Applecross mountains is a Munro (and Corbett); Sgurr a' Chaorachain (774 m) is a Corbett. Heights are not given on the map for the two Grahams shown: Meall Gorm (710 m) and Beinn a'Chlachain (626 m).

5. Wester Ross (the *Game of Thrones* continent is Westeros)

6. Eilean na Ba

7. Milton (author of *Paradise Lost* and *Paradise Regained*)

8. Carn (Cairn) means 'pile of stones' or 'stony hill', whereas Creag means 'rockface' (like crag).

9. Meall Tuath

10. BEALACH NA BA: BEACH outside LA, with A BAN reversed

The Dragon's Spine

1. Llanidloes

2. Penarth

3. Cardiff (*Dr Who* was filmed at BBC Wales' purpose-made studios in Roath Lock, Cardiff Bay)

4. Any two of Swansea, Cardiff, Newport, Llanelli and Barry

5. You would take the A55 from Llandudno towards Chester and then the A48 towards Wrexham until it merges with the A5. Continue on the A5 to Shrewsbury and then take the A49 through Ludlow and towards Monmouth, before finally picking up the A40 and A449 to Cardiff via Newport.

6. Gwydr and Coed-y-Brenin

7. River Dee

8. Mouth (Barmouth, Monmouth, Avonmouth)

9. A458

10. BUILTH WELLS: BUILT HS with WELL inside

The North York Moors

1. *Heartbeat*

2. Rosedale Abbey (the nuns lived in the Priory there)

3. Any two of: Route 617, York to Scarborough; Route 622, York to Hunmanby; Route 620, Easingwold and Filey

4. 46.5 miles (as given in the route detail on p.150)

5. Northallerton

6. Beverley – its Minster is larger than a third of all English cathedrals

7. Esk Dale, Newton Dale, Yorkshire Wolds Way

8. The Cleveland Way

9. 8,777 (= 615 + 616 + 617 + 618 + 622 + 623 + 624 + 625 + 572 + 571 + 518 + 519 + 529 + 535 + 573)

10. SLEIGHTS: EIGHTS on SL (middle letters of ISLE)

The Magic Roundabout

1. The postcode district

2. Drove Road

3. Dougal and Zebedee

4. Euclid Street

5. Three-quarters of a mile (4.75 inches) or 1.21 km (12.1 cm)

6. Gladstone Street

7. One. You can avoid the Magic Roundabout if you start at the western end of Upham Road, turn left into Burford Road, right into Eastern Avenue, left onto Calvert Road, left onto Queen's Drive.

8. 'English Roundabout'

9. Just over a kilometre, or more accurately 1,118 m = $(5 \times \pi \times 46) + (\pi \times 126)$

10. COUNTY ROAD: COUNT (i.e. 'sum') + anagram of OR DAY

Roundabout City

1. V6

2. Fishermead

3. Merlin Walk, Montague Drive, Rooksley

4. Portway or A509

5. They are all named after places in Cornwall

6. Grafton Gate and Secklow Gate

7. Shackleton Place

8. Seven (Summerfield Combined School, Penwith School, Meadfurlong School, The Willow School, Oldbrook First School, Orchard School, Falconhurst Combined School)

9. Midsummer Boulevard and Midsummer Place Shopping Centre

10. GRAFTON GATE: RAFT in GONG + ATE

Spaghetti Junction

1. Tame Valley Canal, Grand Union Canal and the Birmingham and Fazeley Canal

2. Lichfield

3. River Tame

4. 3,533 (found by adding B4516, B4137, B4132 and subtracting A47, A38, A4040 and A5127)

5. Cuckoo Road

6. Gravelly

7. 19,231 strands (you have to round up to the nearest whole strand)

8. 86,666,667 bowls (1 tonne equals 1,000 kg. There would be 6,667 bowls in one tonne).

9. Nechelles

10. STONECHAT DRIVE: ST (saint) + ONE + CHAT + DRIVE

Hanger Lane Gyratory

1. Just over a mile (3.5 inches)

2. Princes Gardens. Both appear south of the A40, one by West Acton station, the other near the Post Office on Pitshanger Lane.

3. Brent and Ealing

4. The Shamrock Sports Club

5. Westway

6. Hill (Hillcroft Crescent, Hillcrest Road, Park Hill, Hillside Road)

7. Golf Course

8. *Crash*

9. The Central Line

10. PARK ROYAL: PARK + ROY and AL

First Motorway

1. Harold Macmillan

2. False. The speed limit was actually much lower – about 38 mph

3. The River Ribble and the River Darwen

4. The M6. Running from junction 19 of the M1 at Rugby, to junction 45 at Gretna, it is 232 miles (374 km) long.

5. It's the boundary line between Lancashire and the metropolitan county of Merseyside.

6. Skelmersdale

7. Leyland

8. Traffic cones

9. 18 miles (4.5 inches). Using the mileage numbers also allows you calculate this: 3 miles (Preston to M55 J1) + 7 miles (M55 J1-3) + 4 miles (M55 J3-4) + 4 miles (M55 J4 to Blackpool).

10. WALTON-LE-DALE: WALTON + LED + ALE

Strangest Bypass

1. Bray (Braywick, Bray Road and Brayfield Road)

2. MAIDENHEAD RFC: anagram of MADE ARCH-FIEND

3. Windsor Road

4. Great West Road (A4) – *see Puzzle 8*

5. Moor Cut is to the east (the clue is Moorbridge Road) and York Stream is to the west (it passes through York Road)

6. Grenfell Park

7. 1.1 miles

8. Ascot

9. Marlow (hence Marlow Road on the map)

10. SAINT-CLOUD WAY: anagram of CONDUIT ALWAYS

Longest Straight Road

1. Lincolnshire

2. Gainsborough

3. Laughterton and Laughton

4. Little Chef. The three shown are near Nettleham, Drisney Nook, and Spital in the Street.

5. The symbol denotes a showground; in this case Lincolnshire Showground.

6. Jerusalem

7. Saxby to Kexby is the greater at c.7.5 miles (12 km) while Wrawby to Scawby is c.3.7 miles (6 km).

8. East Stockwith and West Stockwith; East Ferry and Owston Ferry; East Butterwick and West Butterwick

9. Gainsthorpe Medieval Village

10. HACKTHORN: HACK + THO + RN

Steepest Road

1. Westmoreland, Cumberland and Lancashire

2. Scafell Pike (978 m)

3. 13 miles (20.9 km)

4. Tarns (a lake or pond found in a cirque created by glacial action)

5. Harter Fell

6. Coniston Water

7. Furness Abbey, in Barrow-in-Furness

8. 468 (= 39.3 + 393 + 485 – 803)

9. Kirkstone Pass Inn

10. FURNESS FELLS: NESS FELL in FURS

Bendiest Road

1. Colours (Green Lines, Black Lane and White Sheet Hill)

2. Dorset–Wiltshire

3. Cranborne Chase

4. Thomas Hardy

5. Blackmore Vale

6. Gold Hill

7. Centripetal force

8. Centrifugal force

9. Breeze Hill (262 m)

10. CANN COMMON: COMM(A) in CANNON

Highest Road

1. Glen Beag, Glen Taitneach and Glen Carnach

2. It's a shortening from the Middle English meaning 'hospital' and usually indicates the site of an old abbey (as in the case of Spittal of Glenshee and Spitalfields in London), or somewhere that travellers could rest and receive 'hospitality'.

3. Cairngorms

4. The Cairnwell (932 m)

5. Red deer. Caenlochan Forest, like Balmoral Forest, is a 'deer forest'.

6. Tarn

7. 6 miles

8. Perthshire and Aberdeenshire

9. Braemar Castle

10. BALMORAL: BAL(L) + MORAL